GUIDELINES FOR

TECHNICAL MANAGEMENT OF CHEMICAL PROCESS SAFETY

Publications Available from the
CENTER FOR CHEMICAL PROCESS SAFETY
of the
AMERICAN INSTITUTE OF CHEMICAL ENGINEERS

Guidelines for Technical Management of Chemical Process Safety

Guidelines for Chemical Process Quantitative Risk Analysis

Guidelines for Process Equipment Reliability Data with Data Tables

Guidelines for Vapor Release Mitigation

Guidelines for Safe Storage and Handling of High Toxic Hazard Materials

Guidelines for Use of Vapor Cloud Dispersion Models

Workbook of Test Cases for Vapor Cloud Source Dispersion Models

Guidelines for Hazard Evaluation Procedures

Proceedings of the International Symposium on Runaway Reactions, 1989

Proceedings of the International Conference on Vapor Cloud Modeling, 1987

Proceedings of the International Symposium on Preventing Major Chemical Accidents, 1987

GUIDELINES FOR

TECHNICAL MANAGEMENT OF CHEMICAL PROCESS SAFETY

CENTER FOR CHEMICAL PROCESS SAFETY

of the

American Institute of Chemical Engineers

345 East 47th Street, New York, NY 10017

Library of Congress Cataloging-in-Publication Data

Guidelines for technical management of chemical process safety.
p. cm.
Bibliography: p.
Includes index.
ISBN 0-8169-0423-5
1. Chemical plants—Safety measures. I. American Institute of Chemical Engineers Center for Chemical Process Safety.
TP155.5.G785 1989
660'.284—dc20 89-15866
CIP

This book is available at a special discount when ordered in bulk quantities. For information, contact the Center for Chemical Process Safety at the address shown above.

CONTENTS

LIST OF FIGURES

LIST OF TABLES

Foreword

CCPS recognized from its very beginning that to prevent catastrophic events, such as that at Bhopal, enchancements in chemical process technologies alone would not be enough. With the support of its Advisory and Managing Boards, a multifaceted program was established by CCPS to address the need for technical management commitment and technical management systems in industry to reduce potential exposures to the public and the environment. This CCPS program began several years ago, long before it was to receive the attention being given it today by many organizations and regulatory agencies. More importantly, none of the activities recently initiated by these organizations and agencies offers the scope or depth of the program undertaken by CCPS.

The first document produced was a brochure entitled "A Challenge to Commitment." Under the CCPS program, it provided an overview and an outline of a comprehensive model for the technical management of chemical process safety. This model was characterized by 12 distinct and essential elements. That overview brochure was mailed to more than 1,500 CEOs.

These Guidelines are an expansion of the 12 elements of the CCPS model and provide the framework and detailed components of the CCPS Chemical Process Safety Management System. This book discusses the various alternatives for implementation of each of the elements and components of the CCPS model.

This Guidelines document has been subjected to scrutiny by outside peer reviewers and organizations well versed in the field of chemical process safety. The CCPS Technical Management Subcommittee and peer reviewers represent well over 500 years of professional experience in chemical process safety, and as such they constituted a unique resource for preparing such guidance.

It is gratifying to us at CCPS that, based on exhaustive literature searches and hours of discussions with many companies and organizations, these Guidelines are truly unique. For the first time, all of the essential elements and components of a model of a technical management program in chemical process safety have been assembled in one document. We believe these Guidelines provide the umbrella under which all other CCPS Technical Guidelines will be promulgated.

In the near future, CCPS will publish another book containing more detailed Guidelines or "how-to" materials for plant use. Both this middle management and future plant management guidelines will be supplemented by hands-on training programs under development by CCPS.

CCPS is also actively involved in the development of international symposia to provide opportunities for technology exchanges. In addition, through these projects, CCPS has identified several gaps in chemical process safety technology and management systems. Research and development programs are being initiated to fill these voids.

This subject is not a static one. These Guidelines represent only a snapshot of the latest methods in implementing the technical management of chemical process safety. We encourage all companies and readers of these Guidelines to make suggestions or report on innovative changes or needed research to CCPS, so that these management practices and procedures can continue to be improved in the years ahead.

Thomas W. Carmody
Director
Center for Chemical Process Safety

Acknowledgments

The Center for Chemical Process Safety (CCPS) wishes to thank all the members of the Technical Management Subcommittee who provided guidance in the preparation of these materials. CCPS also wishes to express its appreciation to members of the Technical Steering Committee for their advice and support.

The Technical Management Subcommittee included the following individuals: Joseph C. Sweeney (Chairman, ARCO Chemical Company); Sandy Schreiber and Ray Witter (AIChE staff members); Raymond L. Brandes Jr. (ICI Americas, Inc.); Arthur F. Burk (DuPont); Stan Englund (Dow Chemical, U.S.A.); W.J. Fraser (Merck & Co., Inc.); Wayne Love (The Goodyear Tire and Rubber Company); Thomas L. Rogstad (Union Carbide Corporation); Stanley J. Schechter (Rohm and Haas Company); Wayne E. Scheimann, P.E. (Nalco Chemical Company); Thomas A. Selders (Atlantic Richfield Co.); Mel Turetzky (IBM Corporation); Dennis E. Wade (Monsanto Company); and C.R. West (PPG Industries, Inc.).

Arthur D. Little, Inc., Cambridge, Massachusetts, was the contractor who prepared these Guidelines. Mr. R. Scott Stricoff was Arthur D. Little's Project Director. The principal authors were: Lisa M. Bendixen, Paul A. Croce, J. Ladd Greeno, Thomas McKelvey, Henry Ozog, Stephen Poltorzycki, R. Peter Stickles, and R. Scott Stricoff. Linda M. Nappi's exceptional dedication and skill in manuscript preparation were invaluable.

We gratefully acknowledge the comments and suggestions submitted by the following companies and peer reviewers: Mel Bode (Rohm and Haas Co.); Robert S. Cutro (Merck & Co., Inc.); Charles Dancer (Allied-Signal Inc.); John Dowbekin (Exxon Chemical U.S.A.); W. Fast (PPG Industries, Inc.); Jeffrey Fleming (Hercules Incorporated); Dennis Hendershot (Rohm and Haas Co.); Thomas Howe (The MAC Group); J. Crawford B. MacKeand (ICI Americas Inc.); Steven T. Maher (Westinghouse Electric Corp.); Robert W. Ormsby (Air Products); Gary A. Page (American Cyanamide); John Sharkey (Merck & Co., Inc.); and Chris Smith (Union Carbide Corp).

Glossary

Equipment reliability: The probability that, when operating under stated environmental conditions, process equipment will perform its intended function adequately for a specified exposure period.

Failure mode and effects analysis: A hazard identification technique in which all known failure modes of components or features of a system are considered in turn and undesired outcomes are noted.

Fault tree: A method for representing the logical combinations of various system states that lead to a particular outcome (top event).

Fault tree analysis: Estimation of the hazardous incident (top event) frequency from a logic model of the failure mechanisms of a system.

Hazard: A chemical or physical condition that has the potential for causing damage to people, property, or the environment.

Hazard and Operability Study (HAZOP): A technique to identify process hazards and potential operating problems using a series of guide words to study process deviations.

Historical incident data: Data collected and recorded from past incidents.

Historical error: Actions by designers, operators, or managers that may contribute to or result in accidents.

Human factors: A discipline concerned with designing machines, operations, and work environments so that they match human capacities and limitations.

Human reliability: The study of human errors.

Incident: The loss of containment of material or energy.

Risk: A measure of economic loss or human injury in terms of both the incident likelihood and the magnitude of the loss of injury.

Risk analysis: The development of a qualitative or quantitative estimate of risk based on engineering evaluation and techniques for considering estimates of incident consequences and frequencies.

Risk assessment: The process by which the results of a risk analysis (i.e., risk estimates) are used to make decisions, either through relative ranking of risk reduction strategies or through comparison with risk targets.

Risk management: The systematic application of management policies, procedures, and practices to the tasks of analyzing, assessing, and controlling risk in order to protect employees, the general public, and the environment as well as company assets, while avoiding business interruptions.

1
Introduction

1.1 Process Safety Management Activities of the CCPS

In 1985, the American Institute of Chemical Engineers formed the Center for Chemical Process Safety (CCPS) to promote the improvement of process safety among those who handle, use, process, and store hazardous materials. The first projects supported by CCPS were highly technical in nature. However, CCPS recognized that major accidents could not be prevented by technology-oriented solutions alone. The evolution of process safety from a purely technical issue to one that demanded management approaches was essential to continued process safety improvement.

This book, "Guidelines for the Technical Management of Chemical Process Safety," has been developed by CCPS to present information on the elements of chemical process safety management, and to assist managers in understanding these elements. It is the second of three documents designed to promote the development, implementation, and enhancement of process safety management systems.

An overview brochure, "A Challenge to Commitment," was the first document of this series to be prepared. It introduced the concept of process safety management in terms of the 12 elements listed in Table 1-1. The brochure, which briefly described the elements, was widely distributed to the chief executive officers of those companies that handle or manufacture chemicals.

This book has been written for all managers who have responsibility for chemical processes. This category includes everyone from senior corporate managers to the management staff at facilities. Every manager at each of these levels plays an important role in process safety.

In the third part of the series, this book will be supplemented with a more detailed expansion of the technical guidelines for implementation at plant levels. The third document will provide more specific and detailed guidance to help supervisors implement the program elements described in this book.

1.2 The Need for Process Safety Management

In today's society, the public, customers, in-plant personnel, and government regulatory agencies all demand that companies take necessary actions to reduce the possibility of episodic hazardous materials incidents.

Table 1-1
Twelve Elements of Chemical Process Safety Management

- Accountability: Objectives and Goals
- Process Knowledge and Documentation
- Capital Project Review and Design Procedures
  (for new or existing plants, expansions, and acquisitions)
- Process Risk Management
- Management of Change
- Process and Equipment Integrity
- Incident Investigation
- Training and Performance
- Human Factors
- Standards, Codes, and Laws
- Audits and Corrective Actions
- Enhancement of Process Safety Knowledge

A review of worldwide chemical and petroleum industry safety performance (losses) between 1957 and 1986 (summarized in Figure 1-1) suggests the need for improved approaches to the handling of hazardous materials. A majority of the 100 largest property losses of these industries (on an adjusted, constant dollar basis) occurred during the last 10 years. Reversing this trend toward increasing numbers of larger losses will require new initiatives.

Indeed, during the last 15 years we have seen the occurrence of a number of major chemical or chemical-related incidents that have had major impacts on surrounding communities. A few of these incidents, which have become "household words" as symbols of the potential downside of technologies, are summarized in Table 1-2.

As the chemical process industries have developed more sophisticated ways to improve process safety, we have seen the introduction of safety management systems to augment process safety engineering activities. This document describes how to use management approaches in process safety.

Management systems for chemical process safety are comprehensive sets of policies, procedures, and practices designed to ensure that barriers to major incidents are in place, in use, and effective. The management systems serve to integrate process safety concepts into the ongoing activities of everyone involved in operations -- from the chemical process operator to the chief executive officer.

Prevention of chemical process accidents requires the implementation of effective, comprehensive process safety management systems. Effective process safety management systems can, and do, vary a great deal in how they are implemented. However, they always address the need for managing the process safety-related aspects of technology, facilities, personnel, hazardous materials, and emergency responses.

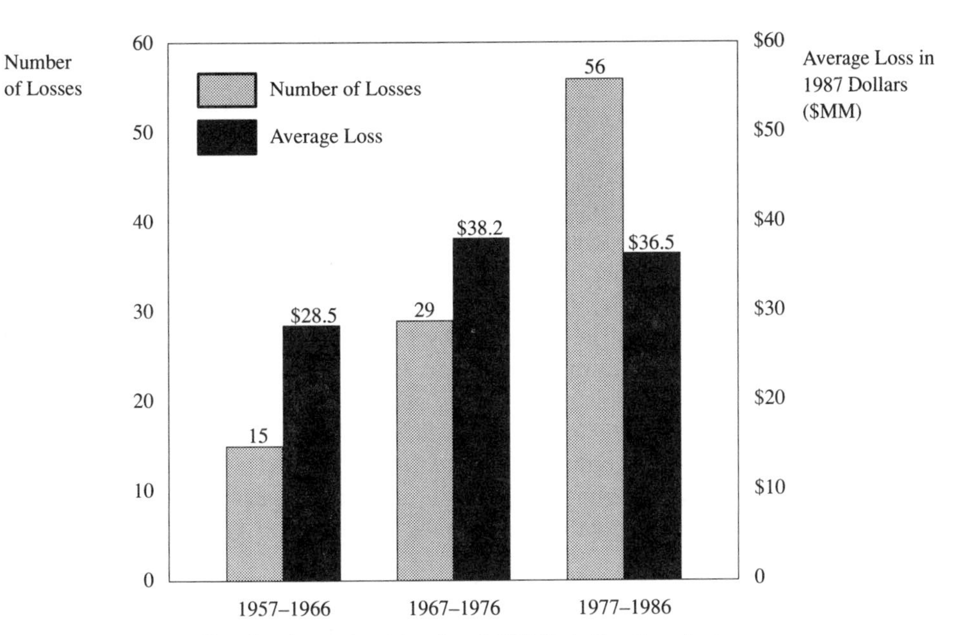

Figure 1–1. *One Hundred Largest Property Damage Losses in the Hydrocarbon-Chemical Industries (1957–1986)*

Table 1-2
Selected Major Incidents

Incident	*Impact*
Flixborough (1974) Vapor cloud explosion	28 fatalities on-site; $232 million damage; damage to homes off-site
Seveso (1976) Toxic material release	Widespread contamination on-site and off-site
Mexico City LPG (1984) LPG explosion	300 fatalities, mostly off-site; $20 million damage
Bhopal (1984) Toxic material release	2500 fatalities off-site; many others injured off-site
Chernobyl (1986) Fire and radiation release	31 fatalities; 300 square miles evacuated; widespread contamination
Sandoz warehouse (1986) Toxic material release	Major impact on ecology of Rhine River
Shell Norco refinery (1988) Vapor cloud explosion	7 fatalities on-site; neighboring town evacuated; widespread damage to homes off-site; damage exceeded $50 million

1.3 What is "Process Safety Management"?

Process safety management differs from the personnel safety activities that have been in place in industry for many years.

Process safety is the operation of facilities that handle, use, process, or store hazardous materials in a manner free from episodic or catastrophic incidents. However, the handling, use, processing, and storage of materials with inherent hazardous properties can never be done in the total absence of risk. In other words, process safety is an ideal condition toward which one strives. Process safety is a dynamic condition involving the technology, materials, people, and equipment that comprise a facility. Process safety management ensures that a properly designed facility is kept that way, and is operated according to the safe manner intended.

Process safety management is the application of management systems to the identification, understanding, and control of process hazards to prevent process-related injuries and incidents.

Process safety management must include consideration of 12 key technical elements, each of which is the subject of a chapter of this book. The 12 elements of chemical process safety management represent a convenient way of grouping 68 components (listed in Table 1-3).

While consideration of these 68 components in the design and implementation of a process safety management system is critical, their organization into 12 elements is simply a convenient way of thinking about them. This book discusses process safety management in terms of the 12 elements; however, alternative ways of organizing the same components can be postulated. The structure and titles used within a company's process safety management system are not important, so long as the appropriate content is present.

While it is clear that certain components may not be relevant in every situation, a comprehensive process safety management program must make provisions for addressing each of the components.

1.4 Scope of These Guidelines

This book describes the technical elements of chemical process safety management. Each of these elements must be considered in the development of a process safety management program. Such a program plays a key role in reducing the risk of chemical accidents.

The 12 process safety elements are described within the context of plant design, construction, startup, operation, maintenance, modification, and decommissioning. Transportation issues outside of the fenceline are not addressed, nor is community emergency response.

As noted earlier, process safety in these guidelines deals with the prevention of episodic or catastrophic incidents from processes that involve the handling, use, processing, or storage of hazardous chemicals. However, the term "process safety" as used in this book does not include personnel safety issues (e.g., slips, trips, and falls) or security issues (e.g., theft) that may occur at chemical process operations, nor does it encompass chronic releases to the environment (although those issues are generally

Table 1-3
Elements and Components of Process Safety Management

1. Accountability: Objectives and Goals
   - Continuity of Operations
   - Continuity of Systems (resources and funding)
   - Continuity of Organizations
   - Company Expectations (vision or master plan)
   - Quality Process
   - Control of Exceptions
   - Alternative Methods (performance vs. specification)
   - Management Accessibility
   - Communications
2. Process Knowledge and Documentation
   - Process Definition and Design Criteria
   - Process and Equipment Design
   - Company Memory (management information)
   - Documentation of Risk Management Decisions
   - Protective Systems
   - Normal and Upset Conditions
   - Chemical and Occupational Health Hazards
3. Capital Project Review and Design Procedures (for new or existing plants, expansions, and acquisitions)
   - Appropriation Request Procedures
   - Risk Assessment for Investment Purposes
   - Hazards Review (including worst credible cases)
   - Siting (relative to risk management)
   - Plot Plan
   - Process Design and Review Procedures
   - Project Management Procedures
4. Process Risk Management
   - Hazard Identification
   - Risk Assessment of Existing Operations
   - Reduction of Risk
   - Residual Risk Management (in-plant emergency response and mitigation)
   - Process Management during Emergencies
   - Encouraging Client and Supplier Companies to Adopt Similar Risk Management Practices
   - Selection of Businesses with Acceptable Risks
5. Management of Change
   - Change of Technology
   - Change of Facility
   - Organizational Changes That May Have an Impact on Process Safety
   - Variance Procedures
   - Temporary Changes
   - Permanent Changes
6. Process and Equipment Integrity
   - Reliability Engineering
   - Materials of Construction
   - Fabrication and Inspection Procedures
   - Installation Procedures
   - Preventive Maintenance
   - Process, Hardware, and Systems Inspections and Testing (pre-startup safety review)
   - Maintenance Procedures
   - Alarm and Instrument Management
   - Demolition Procedures
7. Human Factors
   - Human Error Assessment
   - Operator/Process and Equipment Interfaces
   - Administrative Controls versus Hardware
8. Training and Performance
   - Definition of Skills and Knowledge
   - Training Programs (e.g., new employees, contractors, technical employees)
   - Design of Operating and Maintenance Procedures
   - Initial Qualification Assessment
   - Ongoing Performance and Refresher Training
   - Instructor Program
   - Records Management
9. Incident Investigation
   - Major Incidents
   - Near-miss Reporting
   - Follow-up and Resolution
   - Communication
   - Incident Recording
   - Third-party Participation as Needed
10. Standards, Codes, and Laws
    - Internal Standards, Guidelines, and Practices (past history, flexible performance standards, amendments, and upgrades)
    - External Standards, Guidelines, and Practices
11. Audits and Corrective Actions
    - Process Safety Audits and Compliance Reviews
    - Resolutions and Close-out Procedures
12. Enhancement of Process Safety Knowledge
    - Internal and External Research
    - Improved Predictive Systems
    - Process Safety Reference Library

present wherever chemical process safety is a concern). Although these guidelines do not explicitly address traditional personnel safety or environmental pollution control, there are overlaps between these areas and chemical process safety, as depicted in Figure 1-2.

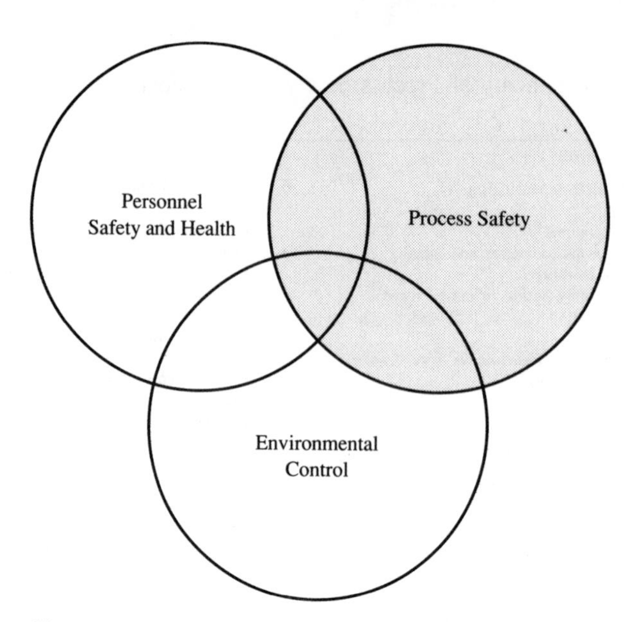

Figure 1–2. *Overlaps Among Safety, Health, and Environmental Areas*

Chemical process technology is found in many places beyond the traditional chemical process industries. The use of new composite materials in aircraft manufacturing, the use of plating and painting operations in automobile production, and the sophisticated manufacturing processes used in making electronic components are but a few examples of the proliferation of chemical process technologies into new areas. The chemical process safety management concepts contained in this book are applicable to all industries where, hazardous chemicals are handled, used, processed, or stored.

1.5 Objective of This Document

The overall objective of this document is to describe each element of process safety management, explain why it is important, and provide information on alternative approaches to the implementation of each element and its components.

This document does not attempt to provide "how-to" implementation detail on the content of process safety management elements. That type of information will be provided in another document being developed as a subsequent project by the CCPS.

The discussions of process safety management elements in this book address the important considerations in managing the elements. The technical content of the elements is not covered in detail by this book, although references to other sources of such information are provided. For example, this book discusses process documentation as an element of process safety management. However, this book does not focus on the contents of process documentation. Rather, the focus of this book is on how process documentation is assembled, and how to assure that it is accurate and complete.

This document is intended to promote rather than limit the creativity of managers in developing management systems that are particularly suitable for their own organizations and operations. Clearly, there is no single "correct" process safety management system applicable universally. This book describes examples of process safety management system implementation; however, those examples are not the only way to address the issue discussed. While a comprehensive management system for chemical process safety will cover each of the 12 elements described in this book, the management system for each facility or organizational unit must be tailored to that specific unit. Each company should adopt a management organization and structure that are appropriate for its culture, its mission, and its business. The process safety management system should then be tailored to that organization and structure.

1.6 Process Safety Management Today

A review of selected large companies (summarized in Figure 1-3) indicates that these firms have implemented some or most of the elements of a comprehensive process safety management system. However, even these firms show room for improvement in the comprehensiveness of their process safety management systems.

Process safety management is an issue that is sure to grow in importance. This book will help managers understand and address their process safety responsibilities.

	Company						
	A	B	C	D	E	F	G
Accountability	●	●	●	●	●	●	●
Documentation	●	◑	◑	◑	○	◑	◑
Capital Project Reviews	◑	◑	◑	◑	◑	◑	◑
Risk Management	●	◑	◑	●	◑	◑	◑
Training	●	●	◑	●	◑	◑	◑
Enhancement	●	●	●	●	○	●	○
Human Factors	●	○	○	○	◑	○	○
Regulations	●	●	○	◑	●	●	◑
Auditing	●	●	●	○	◑	●	◑
Management of Change	◑	◑	◑	●	◑	◑	◑
Process Integrity	●	●	◑	●	◑	◑	◑
Incident Investigation	●	◑	◑	◑	◑	◑	◑

● Element Implemented

◑ Element Partially Implemented (some components)

○ Element Not Implemented

Figure 1–3. *Status of Process Safety Management Systems*

1.7 Organization of This Book

Chapter 2 of this book presents a general description of management systems, and discusses them within the overall context of process safety management. Chapters 3 through 14 each describe one of the elements of chemical process safety management, discussing the importance of the element and the critical management systems issues related to that element.

1.8 How to Use This Book

Process safety management is a complex subject that involves many issues. As a result, any discussion of process safety management may seem intimidating.

In approaching these Guidelines, the reader should recognize that process safety management systems can be implemented in stages. While a comprehensive, integrated system is the objective, it need not be reached in one step.

When beginning the design of a process safety management system, the designer should generally become familiar with the overall contents of this book. It is not necessary to digest each section in detail, but a general understanding of the total scope of process safety management is important background.

Next, the designer should establish priorities for design and implementation. Factors such as the nature of the operations, the hazards present, and the management systems already in place will typically be considered when deciding which components of process safety should be handled first. For example, one might choose to implement a capital project review system as a first stage.

For the component(s) to be handled first, the designer should carefully review the material in these guidelines, critically examine management systems existing in the company, and then begin to develop management systems that address the features and characteristics described in Chapter 2 of this book.

When systems are designed and implemented for the highest priority component(s), the designer should repeat the design process for the next highest priority component(s). New process safety management systems should be linked to and integrated with the systems already put in place.

The amount of information in these Guidelines should not be seen as intimidating. Each step toward a comprehensive process safety management system contributes to enhanced safety performance.

2

Management Systems and the Management of Chemical Process Safety

2.1 Introduction

This chapter provides an overview of management systems theory as applied to chemical process safety. It defines a management system, identifies the functions such a system performs, describes the different levels at which management systems can operate, and discusses the critical role of management leadership. It also raises some of the important considerations that should be borne in mind when adopting and implementing a process safety management system for an organization's own specific needs.

The process safety management concepts presented in this chapter are intended to provide a basic framework that can easily be shaped to fit a company's culture and organizational structure, and to implement a company's policies. These concepts should augment rather than substitute for the management principles and practices already in place in an organization. This chapter is not intended to prescribe an "off-the-shelf" management system that is ready for implementation in all organizational settings.

2.2 The Importance of Leadership

At every level, the critical ingredient in any management system is leadership. Leadership is what drives a management system. For chemical process safety management, leadership is essential to provide visibility, momentum, a sense of organizational commitment and direction, and ultimately reinforcement, through the distribution of rewards and punishments for variable levels of performance. Leadership is needed at every level -- from the CEO to the first-line supervisor. In the absence of strong, effective, continuing leadership, the desired level of safety performance will not be achieved.

2.3 Management Systems: An Overview

Management systems consist of explicit sets of arrangements for planning, organizing, implementing, and controlling work within complex organizations. They are established by managers to assist in achieving their organizations' goals and objectives in an efficient and effective manner.

Management systems may be formal or informal; they may employ extensive written documentation, or use very little of it. For a management system to be effective, its design should consider both the culture, or "style," of the organization within which it will be implemented, and the criticality of the issue(s) being managed.

The process safety management approach should be consistent with the systems used for managing other functions. Process safety management must be integrated with operating management, not segregated from it.

The significance of the issue(s) being managed should also be considered in designing an effective process safety management system. Within the area of chemical process safety, not all elements are equally important, and their relative importance will vary from company to company, plant to plant, and process unit to process unit. For example, an extensive, rigorous system for triggering and reviewing changes to process operating parameters may be appropriate where energy-releasing polymerization reactions are performed. However, where simple blending of non-reactive materials is being done, such a system might be less critical.

There are many ways of describing management systems. For example, Anthony, Dermer, Eilon (References 5,19,22), and many others have published management system "models". Examples are found in many of the books referenced in the Bibliography. No single management system description is right or wrong; different management system models are simply alternative ways of trying to explain the same ideas. One useful way to look at management systems is to perceive that they typically carry out four basic functions: planning, organizing, implementing, and controlling. These functions are interdependent and, as shown in Figure 2-1, they are carried out in a closed loop.

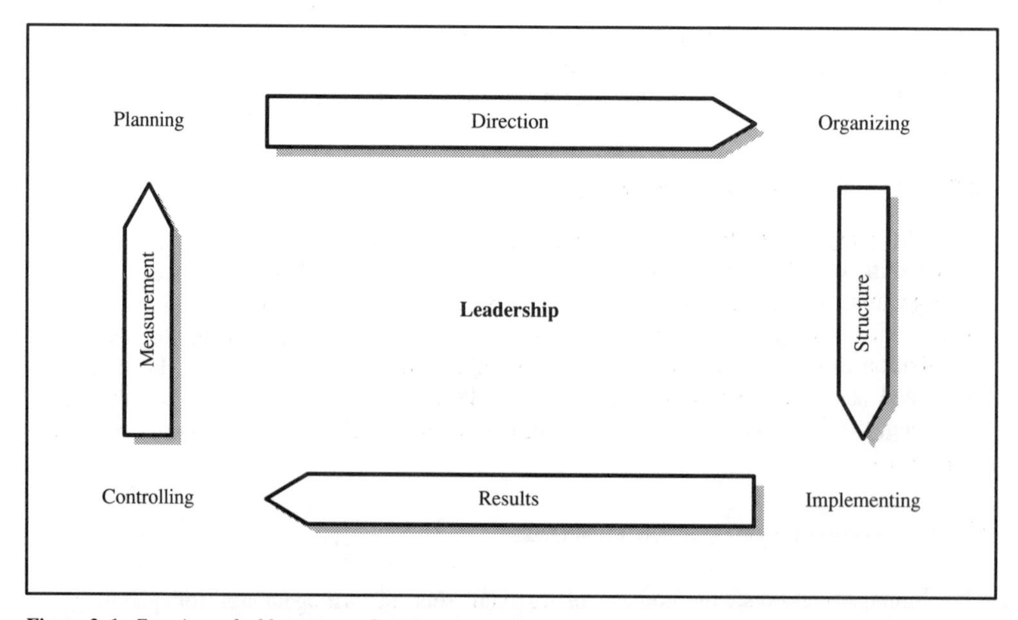

Figure 2–1. *Functions of a Management System*

The planning function includes the need for policy development by senior management. It also involves establishing company goals and objectives, developing strategies for their achievement, and allocating resources to carry out those strategies. Planning establishes the overall direction for the company. For example, in process safety, planning might include assigning resources for the conduct of process hazard reviews.

The organizing function provides the structure and delineates the roles, responsibilities, authority, and accountability for accomplishing the work. Organizing creates the basis for effectively directing and coordinating company resources. Establishing specific process safety objectives for line managers as individual performance targets (e.g., a target might be "completion of process hazard reviews on two units of a plant") is an example of an organizing activity.

The implementing function provides the initiating mechanisms and executes the work effort. Implementing determines the company's results. Establishing mechanisms for triggering and conducting process hazard reviews would be an example of implementing.

The controlling function provides the framework for measuring, evaluating, and correcting implementation performance. Controlling keeps the company on track. A system for tracking resolution of a process hazard review's recommendations is an example of controlling.

Management systems perform these functions on at least three different planes within an organization. At the highest level, management systems are primarily concerned with strategic issues: establishing or revising the goals of the company and identifying the strategies and resources for achieving them. In the middle ranks, the systems exist mainly to provide tactical information and support to help influence other members of the organization. At the task-oriented levels, management systems seek to assure that specific work assignments are carried out efficiently and effectively. Figure 2-2 illustrates the relatively differing emphases among the four basic functions of a management system that are typical on each of these levels.

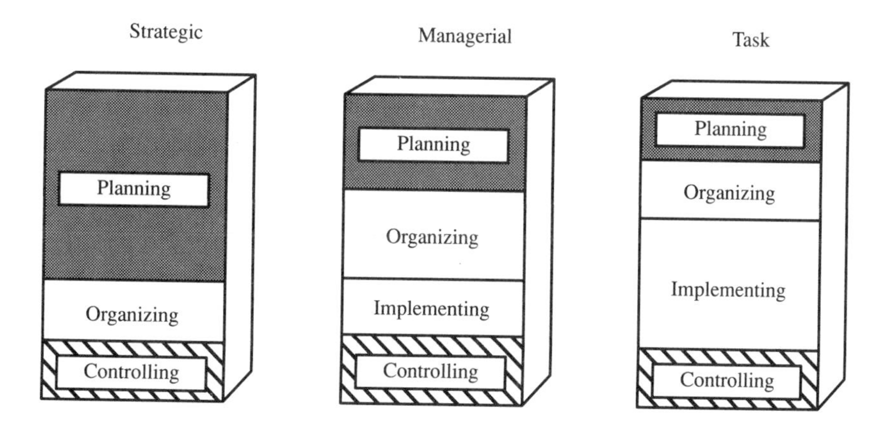

Figure 2–2. *Relative Importance of the Basic Functions*

2.4 Management Systems for Chemical Process Safety

Chemical process safety requires management systems to provide sound facility design, construction, operation, and maintenance. The management systems serve to assure that appropriate organizational resources are made available and used productively and efficiently. They also assure the establishment of overall process safety goals and the integration of these goals with business and other strategic organizational goals. In addition, process safety management systems provide appropriate checks and balances to ensure that the various tactical and task-level functions are carried out as intended.

At the strategic level, process safety management systems are concerned with establishing and reviewing the overall process safety goals and policies of the organization. For example, process safety management systems would involve consideration of the acceptability of the risks associated with major corporate acquisitions, new products, and new processes.

At the tactical level, the process safety management systems are focused on providing information and decision support for assuring that process operations are conducted in a safe manner. A system for verifying that a process safety review has been performed in conjunction with a capital expenditure is an example of a tactical level system.

At the task level, process safety management systems aim to control the regular, ongoing activities. At this level, they attempt to create routine mechanisms for actions and to identify any exceptions for individual attention. An example is the use of a checklist for performing a capital project safety review.

Table 2-1 lists selected examples of the differing types of management system concerns regarding chemical process safety at these three organizational levels.

Table 2-1
Examples of Chemical Process Safety Management System Concerns at Different Organizational Levels

Strategic Level	*Tactical Level*	*Task Level*
Selection of business with acceptable risk	Capital project review procedures	Capital project reviews
Facility expansion	Process and equipment change procedures	SOPs, operator training
Establish policy	Assure compliance	Write procedures

A management system comprises a number of key characteristics. These characteristics, listed in Table 2-2, are generic and apply to systems for managing virtually any important business activity. The characteristics are described in Appendix A.

While the management system characteristics are generic, they have particular applicability to chemical process safety management systems. The following

Table 2-2
Features and Characteristics of a Management System for Chemical Process Safety

---

Planning

Explicit Goals and Objectives
Well-defined Scope
Clear-cut Desired Outputs
Consideration of Alternative Achievement Mechanisms
Well-defined Inputs and Resource Requirements
Identification of Needed Tools and Training

Organizing

Strong Sponsorship
Clear Lines of Authority
Explicit Assignments of Roles and Responsibilities
Formal Procedures
Internal Coordination and Communication

Implementing

Detailed Work Plans
Specific Milestones for Accomplishments
Initiating Mechanisms

Controlling

Performance Standards and Measurement Methods
Checks and Balances
Performance Measurement and Reporting
Internal Reviews
Variance Procedures
Audit Mechanisms
Corrective Action Mechanisms
Procedure Renewal and Reauthorization

---

subsections provide a few specific examples of selected management system characteristics and show how they apply to process safety.

2.4.1 *Planning*

Explicit Goals and Objectives. Managing any element of chemical process safety should start with a clear statement of goals and objectives. Goals establish the desired outcome of the activity--the end state the company wants to achieve. Goal statements can be qualitative (e.g., manage operating risks so as to reduce potential future liability) or quantitative (e.g., accept no event with an expected value greater than 10^{-6} per year). Objectives then translate the goal into more specific statements of purpose -- what it is the company is trying to gain from the activity. For example, an objective might be reduced downtime from unplanned maintenance.

2.4.2 *Organizing*

Internal Coordination and Communication. Well-designed management systems seek to eliminate organizational barriers to the coordination of process safety-related activities across functional specialty lines, and to actively promote close working relationships among operating, maintenance, engineering, research and development, medical, legal, safety, and environmental personnel within the firm. Organizations characterized by strong formal and informal networks of professionals sharing a process safety consensus are frequently better able to identify potential new sources of hazards, and to respond to them more quickly and efficiently. Organizations that provide mechanisms for the feedback of process safety-related information are more likely to foster strong programs.

2.4.3 *Implementing*

Initiating Mechanisms. A management system for chemical process safety should identify and provide for specific mechanisms that trigger appropriate actions as needed. For example, safety reviews should be triggered at appropriate stages of the capital project design process.

2.4.4 *Controlling*

Variance Procedure. Special circumstances sometimes necessitate departures from established operating procedures, which should be considered and approved through established mechanisms. For example, operation with an interlock mechanism disconnected (e.g., while troubleshooting a problem) should be reviewed in advance through a variance procedure.

When a deviation from normal procedures is to be made, the management system should assure that the risk implications of the deviation will be considered, that special risk controls will be adopted if appropriate, that the extent and duration of the departure from normal procedure will be limited, and that the appropriate manager(s) will approve the deviation.

2.5 Summary

In developing a process safety management system, design parameters will be imposed by the organization within which one is working. For example, the overall company organizational structure, existing systems for policy and procedure development and approval, resource availability for process safety management system development, timeframes available for system development, and existing data bases all influence management system design. However, while working within these design parameters, the special needs of process safety management must be reflected as well.

The following 12 chapters of this book discuss the technical elements of chemical process safety management. Each element is discussed within the overall context of process safety management. It is important to remember that the 12 elements define the substance of a comprehensive chemical process safety management program.

Consideration of one or two of the elements without regard for the others would not result in a comprehensive process safety management program. Similarly, addressing elements of process safety purely from a technical perspective, without regard for management systems, would have only limited impact on process risk.

3

Accountability: Objectives and Goals

3.1 Overview

"Accountability" is the obligation to explain and answer for one's actions that are related to company expectations, objectives, and goals. Because it is associated with positive and negative rewards for actions taken, accountability gives "teeth" to the roles and responsibilities assigned through the management system. Accordingly, it is a powerful element of an effective process safety management system.

Accountability is a characteristic that should be built into each component of a process safety management system. However, "accountability" is also the title used in these Guidelines for a specific set of process safety management components.

The "Accountability" components are:

- Continuity of Operations
- Continuity of Systems
- Continuity of Organization
- Quality Process
- Control of Exceptions
- Alternative Methods
- Management Accessibility
- Communications
- Company Expectations

These nine components have been grouped as a single element since they all relate to assuring continued accountability for process safety management during the changes that inevitably occur over time in any company. Through startups and shutdowns, reorganizations, and personnel reassignments, the "accountability" components help to assure that process safety management retains its importance.

This chapter begins with an overview of how accountability issues pervade a management system -- throughout the planning, organizing, implementing, and controlling of activities. A discussion of each of the specific components of the accountability element is then presented.

3.2 Accountability in Management Systems

3.2.1 Planning for Accountability

Explicit Expectations, Objectives, and Goals

Accountability begins with a clear, explicit, and reasonably specific statement of a company's expectations, objectives, and goals. If company expectations, objectives, and goals are to be met, they must be easily understood. Moreover, if individuals are to be rewarded, or held accountable for the way they live up to their process safety duties and obligations, there should be no confusion as to the purpose of these responsibilities. Reasonable specificity is needed so as to avoid situations where goals are so general that they become subjective and confusing. For this reason, general statements of corporate policy, such as "the company will conduct its business in a manner that does not adversely affect the public or the environment," should be supplemented with more specific goal statements.

Within these parameters, a variety of phrasings may be appropriate, depending on one's corporate culture. For example, goal statements can range from:

- *"Process safety audits must be conducted"*

to

- *"Process safety audits must be conducted. Such audits should address the elements of process safety, use prepared checklists and protocols, and be conducted with an audit frequency that is based on the relative level of risk involved."*

The remaining chapters of this book provide examples of topics often embraced by company process safety expectations, objectives, and goals, including pre-start up safety reviews; reviews of modifications to operations; evaluations of operational hazards caused by the use of hazardous materials; pre-siting safety reviews; reduction of inventories; safety reviews of plant and new and modified equipment design; and investigations of accidents and near-misses.

Clear-cut Desired Outputs

Accountability is further fostered by the establishment of specific measures for desired outcomes, with set targets or desired levels. The specificity of these measures and their connection to benefits to the company promote employee understanding, acceptance, and accountability for process safety. For example, a target for the number of employees who will receive process safety training during the year is concrete and specific. Employees can be motivated by the understanding that safety training helps avoid incidents that adversely affect the community. As Figure 3-1 depicts, establishing targets for program outcome becomes part of an iterative process that promotes improved performance.

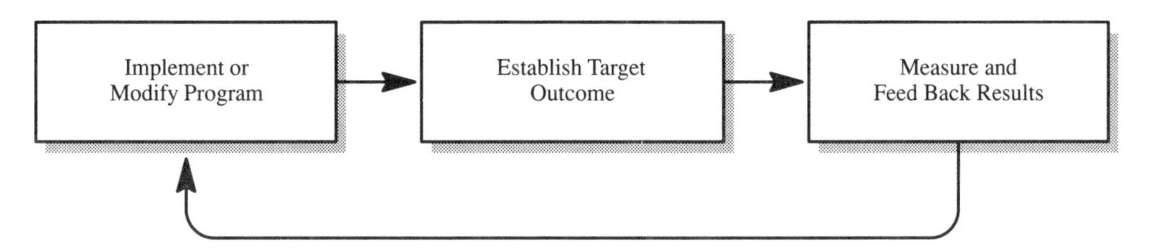

Figure 3–1. *Use of Outcome Targets for Continuous Improvements*

Alternative Achievement Mechanisms

Planning for accountability should take into account alternative methods for meeting company goals and objectives. Although there is often no "right" or "best" way for achieving process safety objectives and goals, accountability is made more difficult when alternative achievement mechanisms exist. In such cases, care must be taken to assure that accountability is not compromised because of the confusion surrounding accountability under a variety of standards within a company.

Well-defined Resource Requirements

A central element of process safety planning is the determination of the types and amount of personnel and the financial and technical resources needed to accomplish process safety goals and objectives. Accountability should be used not only to ensure that resources are properly estimated and allocated when programs are established, but also to ensure that proper resources continue to be made available during the life of a program, including during times of corporate change.

3.2.2 *Organizing for Accountability*

Sponsorship

A key element of a successful process safety management system is the designation of specific persons or positions as responsible for each element of a process safety management program. The lack of such a "sponsor" or "champion" will tend to undermine accountability throughout an organization because of a perception of a lack of accountability for process safety at the top. Effective process safety management requires a strong commitment from senior management, including an acceptance of accountability.

Clear Lines of Authority and Assignments of Roles and Responsibilities

Central to process safety accountability is the delineation of who is responsible for what areas of process safety. A process safety management system falters when individuals who have production or other responsibilities that have an impact on process safety are not explicitly assigned responsibility for process safety matters. The organizational structure, as it sets forth lines of reporting and responsibilities for specific process safety activities, should bring within its scope all employees capable of significantly influencing process safety, and promote understanding and agreement as to individual approval and authorization requirements. Assignments of responsibilities should be made to designated organizational units and individual job titles. Accountability is reinforced through job descriptions, measures of performance, and performance reviews that are tied to process safety performance. For example, one company has tied qualification for bonus and profit-sharing payouts to meeting individually tailored process safety objectives.

Formal Procedures

Accountability can be promoted by the use of formal procedures that specify task sequences for meeting process safety responsibilities. Under such an arrangement, individuals understand exactly what conduct is expected from them and for which activities they are answerable. As there may be a variety of methods for achieving process safety goals, some companies do not employ formal procedures. However, in many companies, formal procedures enhance accountability. For example, Appendix B shows one company's pre-startup safety review procedure, which includes specific task sequences and individual responsibilities.

Communications

Ways must be found to provide the communication and coordination needed for effective process safety management, despite any institutional barriers that may exist. Senior managers should communicate their understanding of their own individual process safety accountability, as well as that of their unit to individuals within the unit. Understanding of the unit's accountability and that of its senior managers promotes individual accountability throughout the unit. In cases where responsibilities may overlap between individuals or units, some companies go so far as to require a written agreement between the concerned individuals and the heads of units as to who is to take the primary responsibility for each component of the activity. Even where more common, less formal mechanisms are used to achieve coordination, it is important to assure that the boundaries between individuals' responsibilities do not become cracks through which process safety issues can slip. For example, Table 3-1 presents a matrix system for ensuring communication and coordination regarding process safety between various functions, such as engineering, safety, operations, and the like.

3.2.3 *Implementing Accountability*

Top management must not only make frequent and clear statements to employees of their expectations for process safety performance, but they must also back these statements up by calling upon employees to account for their actions. For example,

Table 3-1
Example of Communications and Coordination Matrix

Function	*Safety*	*Engineering*	*Operations*	*Maintenance*	*Management*
Incident Investigation	S	S	R	R	A
Employee Educ. & Training (Supvr. & Hourly)	S	S	R	R	A
Process Safety Stds. for Equip., Work Methods, and Products	S	I	R	R	A
Audits to Identify Potential Hazards in Operations	S	I	R	I	A
Fire & Emergency Plans	R	I	R	S	A
Maintenance	I	I	I	R	A
Plant Expansion/New Equipment	I	R	R	S	A

Legend:

A - AUTHORITY (who has the final authority?)
R - RESPONSIBILITY (who is responsible for performing the functions?)
S - SUPPORT (who is expected to support the functions?)
I - INFORMATION (who should be informed of function activities?)

some companies require that key managers provide assurance letters to top management confirming compliance with process safety goals and objectives. If full compliance has not been achieved, exceptions must be specifically stated, with an action plan to achieve compliance.

Accountability for process safety aspects of routine activities can be accomplished through detailed work plans and individualized job objectives, with milestones for accomplishments. A system of positive and negative rewards for meeting, or failing to meet, scheduled milestones is an important element in process safety accountability.

In addition to accountability for routine activities, it is important to have in place well-understood procedures that will trigger process safety accountability for non-routine activities or events. Some companies make it clear that in the event of a significant process safety accident or incident, the facility manager must report--in person--to a senior corporate officer to give an account of the event. Accountability for process safety during non-routine events, such as interruptions to continuous operations, organizational changes, and variances is discussed in Section 3.3.

3.2.4 Controlling Accountability

Performance Measurement and Reporting

A central method of achieving accountability for process safety is to periodically evaluate employee process safety performance. Process safety objectives set forth in job descriptions, work plans, and individualized job objectives (sometimes known as management by objectives --MBOs--or "measures of performance") are common standards against which performance is measured. The evaluation of process safety performance can be a powerful tool for achieving accountability if an effective performance appraisal system is in place. Some companies require that, during the performance appraisal process, the weight given to process safety performance be equal to (or greater than) the weight given to production, quality, sales, and cost performance. A few examples of individual objectives related to process safety are given in Table 3-2.

Audit Mechanisms

Accountability throughout a division, facility, or operating unit is furthered by process safety audits and assessments. These audits examine operating conditions and procedures, process safety systems, and management controls. The results of the audits are communicated to both employees within the facility and to division or corporate management. The audit process is structured so that accountability is necessarily

Table 3-2
Example of Individual Process Safety Performance Objectives

Perform process hazard review of XYZ process unit by end of year.
Implement relief valve inspection and testing program by end of third quarter.
Attend process safety management training program during first quarter.

evoked during both information-gathering interviews and in the discussion of audit findings of non-compliance with company standards, goals, or objectives. In addition to fostering accountability at the plant level, audits promote accountability among senior line managers in that they provide the basis for senior managers to give assurance to senior corporate officers that company process safety goals and objectives are being met in their organizations. Process safety auditing is discussed in detail in Chapter 12.

3.3 Components of the "Accountability" Process Safety Management Element

The element of process safety management referred to as "accountability" actually encompasses a set of issues that are related to continuity. As operations, organizational structures, systems, and personnel change, effective process safety management systems assure that accountability for process safety is not lost.

The following sections discuss the components of process safety management comprising the element "accountability".

3.3.1 Continuity of Operations

Continuity of operations within a plant is often regarded as being principally a production goal. However, circumstances or events that affect continuity of operations have a significant influence on process safety and are often overlooked in systems of accountability. Events and circumstances, such as unplanned shutdowns, lack of shutdowns, shift changes, non-retention of spare parts, and significant changes in production volumes, can all have a negative impact on process safety, particularly in single-train operations.

Unplanned shutdowns can give rise to rushed startups without proper regard to process safety if accountability exists only for production goals. A system of accountability that takes into account process safety during unusual circumstances, such as unplanned shutdowns, is an important part of an effective process safety management program.

Circumstances may arise where a process safety-related shutdown of operations is appropriate, but the accountability system is set up only to discourage production loss. The accountability system should not penalize individuals for a production loss that results from process safety considerations, and should clearly set forth accountability for initiating required process safety-related shutdowns.

Explicit accountability should also exist for process safety considerations during material increases or decreases in production volumes. Such changes in production volume often create a heavier burden on resources in the direction of production activities at the expense of process safety. For example, a temptation to defer important process safety-related training may occur when changes in production volume result in increased workloads. There should be accountability for meeting the planned training targets so that deferral is not begun without full consideration of the implications.

Normally, routine activities, such as a shift change, should include a process safety accountability component. This will ensure internal communications among shift members as to circumstances that may affect process safety. A common procedure is to require shift personnel to use and sign a shift log each day. In the log, the status of equipment and processes is documented, along with any unusual situations or procedures that may have occurred. Under this procedure, incoming shift personnel can quickly be brought up to speed, and there is a written and signed record of the transfer of information. This helps place accountability upon the shift staff for recording all information that could be important to future shifts.

3.3.2 Continuity of Systems

The realities of corporate life are such that resources and funding are always limited; however, the allocation of resources should reflect accountability for process safety. The lack of appropriate capital or resources for process systems may lead to operating deviations that, while meeting production targets, jeopardize process safety.

Accountability for the continuity of process systems in terms of obtaining the resources and funding needed for adequate process safety should involve a level of management beyond the process unit in question. This can be accomplished by assigning process safety accountability to various job functions or units for each phase in the life cycle of a process system from design to demolition. It is vital that this accountability be equally rigorous throughout the life cycle of the process, being determined by the risk of process hazards, not by the economic viability of the process. For example, one company helps ensure continuity of systems by establishing "technology centers"--departments with stewardship and overall accountability for a given technology (including process safety) wherever in the company that technology is used. A technology center helps assure uniformity of operations and communications between plants using the same technology in different locations. It also helps assure that the best technology is used at all plants.

3.3.3 Continuity of Organizations

Changes in organizational structures, such as reporting relationships or changes in senior management personnel, can have a severe impact on process safety accountability. Individuals charged with particular process safety responsibility can move to new roles, and accountability may then be compromised.

Changes are a "given" in the corporate world. Mergers are commonplace, and managements often decide to restructure their companies by way of decentralizing or other organizational changes. An effective system of accountability must be flexible enough to accommodate such an organizational change.

Individuals must be held accountable for their specific job functions in process safety. Continuity of accountability is promoted when accountability attaches to the job function as well as to the individual. This may be accomplished through detailed work plans, job descriptions, individual job objectives, upward reporting of process safety performance measures, or through a combination of these approaches. In cases where job functions are eliminated, those responsible for eliminating the job function should also be responsible for ensuring that the process safety accountability component of the job function survives within the organization. This can be accomplished by use of a task analysis, whereby a list of process safety tasks to be accomplished is prepared, and responsibilities for accomplishing these tasks are assigned throughout the new organizational structure.

Table 3-3 presents a simple example of a task analysis. In this example, the "assistant production superintendent" position is being eliminated, and the task analysis indicates reassignment of accountabilities, assuring that all tasks are accounted for.

When responsibilities are reassigned, it is also important to assure that the remaining personnel are able to perform their new duties. They must have adequate knowledge, experience, and available times to perform their new duties.

3.3.4 Quality Process

Quality, sometimes defined as conformance with specifications, has been the subject of volumes of literature, but it is often not addressed within the context of process safety accountability. Some companies view quality as encompassing both process safety and production in that both production defects and process safety problems are instances of nonconformance with specifications, and are therefore quality problems. Accountability for quality does not fall to quality control/quality assurance departments or individuals alone, but it is a component of every employee's performance. The existing literature on establishing systems for ensuring quality is particularly enlightening on the subject of accountability. Selected references appear in the Bibliography at the end of this book.

Table 3-3
Example of Reassigned Accountability

Previous Accountability	*New Accountability*		
Process Safety Tasks of Assistant Production Superintendent	*Shift Supervisor*	*Production Superintendent*	*Safety Supervisor*
Monitor safety training attendance	X		
Approve process hazard review reports		X	
Participate in capital project safety reviews		X	
Maintain combustible gas indicator			X

3.3.5 Control of Exceptions

Flexibility is an important component of management systems and procedures. Not every situation to which a system or procedure applies can be addressed in accordance with normal procedures. Flexible systems recognize this fact and allow for variances from procedures to be authorized based upon appropriate and logical grounds. However, accountability with respect to process safety in the granting of variances and in following the variance process is often not addressed. Variance procedures are discussed in detail in Chapter 7. However, it is important to keep in mind that because variances entail a change from customary practice, process safety may be jeopardized and process safety accountability should be triggered. Accountability for granting variances may be found at the corporate, division, or plant level depending on the circumstances and level of risk involved, but there should be logic to the process and accountability for process safety.

3.3.6 Alternative Methods

Many companies incline towards performance standards for process safety that identify only the desired result, rather than specification standards that stipulate both the result and the steps that must be taken to achieve that result. While it may be stifling to have overly specific process safety standards, accountability is more difficult to achieve with performance standards than with specification standards. As a result, in companies that use performance standards, an appropriate process safety accountability system will not rely solely on one control measure, such as individualized job objectives, but will utilize several control measures, perhaps employing audits and assurance letters as well as individualized job objectives. For example, there may be a company standard calling for process hazard reviews that leaves the nature and content of the reviews to the operating unit. Creating accountability for meeting this standard should involve more than simply confirming that a review occurred. The quality, comprehensiveness, and timeliness of the review should also be parameters of accountability, and might be measured through an audit process.

Some companies permit divisions or other business units to establish their own standards, providing corporate model standards as guidelines. This approach should take into account situations where the corporate model standard might not apply. In such cases, the division or other unit should be accountable for providing an alternative standard that will meet company expectations, goals, and objectives. For example, the company guideline might provide a suggested checklist for process hazard reviews. The checklist might be inappropriate for one division engaged in a substantially different business from the other divisions. The division with different operations should be accountable for implementing a process hazard review procedure tailored to its own operations.

3.3.7 Management Accessibility

Senior managers with process safety responsibility should be accountable to exercise that responsibility. It is their function to set the expected standards of performance, and to judge that these standards are being met. Process safety responsibilities may be delegated too far down the organizational line; then, when unusual circumstances arise that jeopardize process safety, these managers are not accessible to make decisions that are most appropriately made by persons of their judgment and experience. A successful system of process safety accountability makes managers accountable for being available and accessible to their staff with respect to decisions that will have an impact on process safety.

Successful process safety management also provides for decision-making by responsible senior managers when there are conflicting views among safety, engineering, production, and business managers. There should be clearly understood mechanisms for resolving such conflicts in ways that allow for consideration of all pertinent information.

4

Process Knowledge and Documentation

4.1 Overview

The construction and operation of facilities for the handling, use, production and storage of hazardous chemicals involve a major commitment of company resources. A considerable amount of intellectual equity is acquired over the years as a result of this ownership, which is fundamental to the long-term viability and financial success of a company (e.g., for use in yield improvement or process optimization). However, capturing process knowledge is also the foundation upon which many aspects of a process safety program are built. Preserving and making available this knowledge within a company are both important for process safety for a number of reasons, including:

- Preserving a record of design conditions and materials of construction for existing equipment, which helps assure that operations and maintenance remain faithful to the original intent;
- Allowing recall of the rationale for key design decisions during major capital project, which is useful for a variety of reasons, such as an aid in future projects and modifications;
- Providing a basis for understanding how the process should be operated and why it should be run in a given way;
- Offering a "baseline" for use in evaluating process change;
- Recording accident/incident causes and corrective actions and other operating experience for future guidance;
- Protecting the company against unjustified claims of irresponsibility and negligence; and
- Retaining basic research and development information on process chemistry and hazards to guide future research efforts.

In addition, in some states legislation now requires owners of chemical plants to maintain up-to-date documents and procedures on many aspects of plant design and operation.

This chapter provides guidelines for creating a management system that will ensure the capture and retention of safety-related process knowledge and documentation. The components of this "process knowledge and documentation" element are:

- Chemical and occupational health hazards,
- Process definition and design criteria,
- Process and equipment design,
- Protective systems,
- Normal and upset conditions (operating procedures),
- Process risk management decisions, and
- Company memory.

The components of "process knowledge and documentation" are important throughout the life cycle of an operation (as depicted in Figure 4-1). These components are discussed below, within an order and structure that correspond to the life cycle.

4.2 Chemical and Occupational Health Hazards

The documentation of chemical and occupational health hazards should cover all hazards associated with the various materials involved in the process. This information is vital to safe design and operation throughout the life of the process. Certain information is also required by Federal and State regulations.

The chemical hazards information should be documented in more than one form, reflecting the differing needs of those who will be using the data. For example, for

CHEMICAL PROCESS SAFETY-RELATED TASKS

Project Lifetime

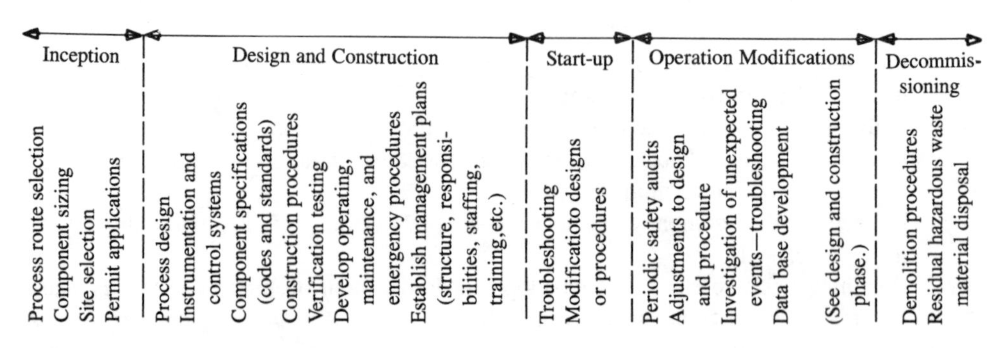

Figure 4.1. *Typical phases in the lifetime of a chemical industry.*

operators and laboratory workers who may work with a chemical, a material safety data sheet (MSDS), such as shown in Figure 4-2, or its equivalent should be available. For those involved in process development and design, additional information on reactivity and chemical and physical properties is important. Table 4-1 shows an example of the contents of a detailed chemical data package for use by process chemists and process engineers. Where mixtures are used, information on the components as well as on the mixture should be available. It is important to note that the contents of a chemical data package will vary significantly from process to process and industry to industry.

It is also important to have a management system that will assure the capture and dissemination of internally generated data or experience on reactivity and toxicological effects. For example, medical and industrial hygiene personnel, as well as production personnel, should be given a mechanism for documenting suspected acute and chronic toxic effects. Newly discovered information on energetic reactions, toxic reaction products, and corrosivity should also be documented. Experimental or plant data on corrosion rates experienced with certain materials also have to be captured.

The chemical hazard data management system must be planned so that it incorporates all of the appropriate information needed, and allows access by the appropriate staff. This planning includes making choices between computerized and manual information systems, either of which may be appropriate depending on the situation. Related organizational issues include providing staff resources to maintain the information (including new information on existing materials), and assuring that

Table 4-1
Example of a Chemical Data Package

- Chemical identification data, such as chemical formula and synonyms
- Physical property data, such as molecular weight, density, boiling point, freezing point, vapor pressure, viscosity, solubility, etc.
- Thermodynamic data, such as reaction heat, latent heat, heat capacity, thermal conductivity
- Reactivity/stability data, such as flash point, flammability limits (or minimum explosive concentration and ignition energy for dusts), spontaneous decomposition or polymerization, shock sensitivity, pyroforicity, hydroforicity, reactivity with common materials of construction, etc.
- Exposure guidelines such as threshold limit value, immediately dangerous to life and health value, emergency response planning guideline levels, etc.
- Regulatory status data, such as OSHA-permissible exposure limits, EPA SARA reporting quantities, DOT classification, EPA RCRA classification, etc.
- Toxicity data, such as LC_{50}, LD_{50}, carcinogenicity, mutagenicity, teratogenicity, and neurotoxicity data, etc.

MATERIAL SAFETY DATA SHEET

EFFECTIVE DATE: 07/01/88

urges each customer or recipient of this MSDS to study it carefully to become aware of and understand the hazards associated with the product. The reader should consider consulting reference works or individuals who are experts in ventilation, toxicology, and fire prevention, as necessary or appropriate to use and understand the data contained in this MSDS.

To promote safe handling, each customer or recipient should: (1) notify its employees, agents, contractors and others whom it knows or believes will use this material of the information in this MSDS and any other information regarding hazards or safety; (2) furnish this same information to each of its customers for the product; and (3) request its customers to notify their employees, customers, and other users of the product of this information.

I. IDENTIFICATION

PRODUCT NAME: METHYL CARBITOL

CHEMICAL NAME: Diethylene Glycol Monomethyl Ether

CHEMICAL FAMILY: Glycol Ethers

FORMULA: CH3O(C2H4O)2H MOLECULAR WEIGHT: 120.2

SYNONYMS: Methoxy Diglycol; 2-(2-Methoxyethoxy) Ethanol

CAS # and 111-77-3
CAS NAME: Ethanol, 2-(2-methoxyethoxy)

II. PHYSICAL DATA

BOILING POINT, 760 mm Hg: 194 C (381.2 F)

FREEZING POINT: -85 C (-121 F)

SPECIFIC GRAVITY(H2O =1): 1.023 @ 20/20C VAPOR PRESSURE AT 20°C: 0.1 mm Hg

---

VAPOR DENSITY (air = 1): 4.14 SOLUBILITY IN WATER by wt: Complete

---

EVAPORATION RATE
(Butyl Acetate = 1): 0.015

APPEARANCE AND ODOR: Colorless liquid, mild odor

PERCENT VOLATILES (BY VOLUME): 100

Figure 4-2 *Example Material Safety Data Sheet*

PRODUCT NAME: METHYL CARBITOL

III. INGREDIENTS

MATERIAL	%	EXPOSURE LIMITS	HAZARD
Diethylene Glycol Monomethyl Ether (111-77-3)	100	None established	Eye irritant; Combustible

IV. FIRE AND EXPLOSION HAZARD DATA

FLASH POINT: 188 F (87 C) Tag Closed Cup; 200 F (93 C) Cleveland Open Cup

FLAMMABLE LIMITS IN AIR, % by volume: LOWER: 1.7 (calc'd) UPPER: 22 (calc'd)

EXTINGUISHING MEDIA: Apply alcohol-type or all-purpose-type foams by manufacturer's recommended techniques for large fires. Use CO2 or dry chemical media for small fires.

SPECIAL FIRE FIGHTING PROCEDURES: Use self-contained breathing apparatus when fighting fires in enclosed areas.

UNUSUAL FIRE AND EXPLOSION HAZARDS: None

V. HEALTH HAZARD DATA

TLV AND SOURCE: None established by ACGIH or OSHA.

EFFECTS OF ACUTE OVEREXPOSURE:

SWALLOWING: Slightly toxic. May produce signs of intoxication characterized by incoordination, dizziness, drowsiness, headache, nausea, mental confusion, possibly slurred speech and stupor, depending on the quantity of materall ingested.

SKIN ABSORPTION: No evidence of adverse effects from available information.

INHALATION: No evidence of adverse effects from available information.

SKIN CONTACT: No evidence of adverse effects from available information.

EYE CONTACT: Causes stinging, pain, and irritation seen as excess redness and swelling of the conjunctiva.

EFFECTS OF REPEATED OVEREXPOSURE: No evidence of adverse effects from available information.

MEDICAL CONDITIONS AGGRAVATED BY OVEREXPOSURE: None currently known

ADDITIONAL TOXICITY INFORMATION: This material caused slight embryofetal toxicity (delayed development) but no increase in birth defects in laboratory animals when applied continuously to the skin during pregnancy.

Figure 4-2 *Example Material Safety Data Sheet (continued)*

PRODUCT NAME: METHYL CARBITOL

EMERGENCY AND FIRST AID PROCEDURES:

SWALLOWING:	If patient is conscious, give two glasses of water and induce vomiting.
SKIN:	Wash with soap and water.
INHALATION:	No emergency care anticipated.
EYES:	Immediately flush eyes thoroughly with water and continue flushing for at least 15 minutes. Seek medical attention.
NOTES TO PHYSICIAN:	There is no specific antidote. Treatment of overexposure should be directed at the control of symptoms and the clinical condition.

VI. REACTIVITY DATA

STABILITY: Stable

CONDITIONS TO AVOID: None

INCOMPATIBILITY (materials to avoid):
Avoid contamination with high concentrations of alkali at elevated temperatures.

HAZARDOUS COMBUSTION OR DECOMPOSITION PRODUCTS:
Burning can produce carbon monoxide and/or carbon dioxide.

HAZARDOUS POLYMERIZATION: Will Not Occur

CONDITIONS TO AVOID: None

VII. SPILL OR LEAK PROCEDURES

STEPS TO BE TAKEN IF MATERIAL IS RELEASED OR SPILLED:
Small spills should be flushed with large quantities of water. Larger spills should be collected for disposal.

WASTE DISPOSAL METHOD: Incinerate in a furnace where permitted under appropriate Federal, State and local regulations. Also, see Section IX.

VIII. SPECIAL PROTECTION INFORMATION

RESPIRATORY PROTECTION:
None required in normal use.

VENTILATION: General (mechanical) room ventilation is expected to be satisfactory.

PROTECTIVE GLOVES: Plastic gloves

Figure 4-2 *Example Material Safety Data Sheet (continued)*

PRODUCT NAME: METHYL CARBITOL

EYE PROTECTION: Safety glasses

OTHER PROTECTIVE EQUIPMENT:
Eye bath, safety shower

IX. SPECIAL PRECAUTIONS

PRECAUTIONS TO BE TAKEN IN HANDLING AND STORAGE:
CAUTION! May cause eye irritation.
Combustible.

Avoid contact with eyes.
Keep away from heat and flame.
Keep container closed.
Use with adequate ventilation.
FOR INDUSTRY USE ONLY

OTHER PRECAUTIONS: In very dilute solution, this product can be biodegraded in an activated sludge biological waste treatment system.

X. REGULATORY INFORMATION

STATUS ON SUBSTANCE LISTS:

The concentrations shown are maximum or ceiling levels (weight %) to be used for calculations for regulations. Trade Secrets are indicated by "TS".

FEDERAL EPA

Comprehensive Environmental Response, Compensation, and Liability Act of 1980 (CERCLA) requires notification of the National Response Center of release of quantities of Hazardous Substances equal to or greater than the reportable quantities (RQs) in 40 CFR 302.4.

Components present in this product at a level which could require reporting under the statute are:
None

Superfund Amendments and Reauthorization Act of 1986 (SARA) Title III
requires emergency planning based on Threshold Planning Quantities (TPQs) and release reporting based on Reportable Quantities (RQs) in 40 CFR 355 (used for SARA 302, 304, 311 and 312).

Components present in this product at a level which could require reporting under the statute are:
None

Superfund Amendments and Reauthorization Act of 1986 (SARA) Title III
requires submission of annual reports of release of toxic chemicals that appear in 40 CFR 372 (for SARA 313). This information must be included in all MSDSs that are copied and distributed for this material.

Components present in this product at a level which could require reporting under the statute are:

CHEMICAL	CAS NUMBER	UPPER BOUND CONCENTRATION %
Glycol Ethers	N/A	100

STATE RIGHT-TO-KNOW

CALIFORNIA Proposition 65
None

Figure 4-2 *Example Material Safety Data Sheet (continued)*

PRODUCT NAME: METHYL CARBITOL

MASSACHUSETTS Right-To-Know, Substance List (MSL) Hazardous Substances and Extraordinarily Hazardous Substances on the MSL must be identified when present in products.

Components present in this product at a level which could require reporting under the statute are:

HAZARDOUS SUBSTANCES (=> 1%)

CHEMICAL	CAS NUMBER	UPPER BOUND CONCENTRATION %
Diethylene Glycol Monomethyl Ether	111-77-3	100

PENNSYLVANIA Right-To-Know, Hazardous Substance List Hazardous Substances and Special Hazardous Substances on the List must be identified when present in products.

Components present in this product at a level which could require reporting under the statute are:

HAZARDOUS SUBSTANCES (=> 1%)

CHEMICAL	CAS NUMBER	UPPER BOUND CONCENTRATION %
Diethylene Glycol Monomethyl Ether	111-77-3	100

Toxic Substances Control Act(TSCA) STATUS:

The ingredients of this product are on the TSCA inventory.

CALIFORNIA SCAQMD RULE 443.1 VOC'S:

VOC 1021 g/L; Vapor Pressure 0.1 mm Hg @ 20C

OTHER REGULATORY INFORMATION:

None

Date: 03/13/89
Revision Date: 03/14/89 Printed in USA
PC: 46702
F NUMBER: C0314

Figure 4-2 *Example Material Safety Data Sheet (continued)*

responsibility is assigned for acquiring information on new materials as they become subjects of interest to the research, manufacturing, or business functions.

Implementation of the chemical hazard data management system also involves assuring that everyone who may need access to chemical data knows how to both acquire and interpret the data. Control of this system requires assuring that the data entered into the system over time remains current and accurate. Management of the system requires defined responsibilities and inclusion of the system in appropriate auditing programs.

4.3 Process Definition/Design Criteria

Process safety documentation should include the basic process knowledge and design considerations that form the foundation for facility design and operation. Prior to design, it is essential that this process safety documentation be as complete as possible, since the identification and mitigation of potential process hazards will be developed from this information. As subsequent knowledge is obtained or developed as a result of process or technology modification, it should also be incorporated into the documentation and carefully reviewed.

The first aspect of this documentation is the process definition. (This is given other names specific to individual firms, but will be referred to as "process definition" herein for simplicity.) The process definition should include the fundamental process chemistry and conceptual process flow configuration, including major steps or unit operations to the extent known. Table 4-2 lists the contents of a typical process definition.

The process definition should be documented in a single document or single set of documents, bringing all process-related information together. The management system for this component must reflect many considerations.

Table 4-2
Example of Process Definition Contents

- Chemical reactions and equations for primary and important secondary or side reactions
- Type and nature of catalysts used
- Competing side reactions
- Reactive chemical data on all streams, including in-process chemicals
- Kinetics data for important process reactions, including order, rate constants vs. time, approach to equilibrium, etc.
- Kinetics data for undesirable reactions, such as decompositions and auto-polymerizations
- Process boundaries stated in terms of pressure, temperature, concentration, feed-to-catalyst ratio, etc., along with description of the consequences of operating beyond these limits
- Process steps or unit operations involved, starting with raw material storage and feed preparation and ending with product recovery and storage
- Where possible, a preliminary process flow diagram (PFD) indicating pressures, temperatures, and compositions of principal streams at various locations
- Major material inventories required
- Description of general control philosophy, i.e., identifying the primary control variables and the reasons for their selection
- Discussion of special design considerations that are required because of the unique hazards or properties of the chemicals involved. Examples of special design considerations might include:
  - Use of non-lubricated equipment in oxygen service.
  - Use of dedicated, high-purity nitrogen to avoid water/oxygen contamination of certain reactive molecules.
  - Use of intermediate, non-aqueous cooling or heating fluids with hydrofluoric or water- catalyzed materials to eliminate hazards of exchanger leaks.

Organizing issues related to process definition documentation begins with the assignment of responsibility for compiling and maintaining the process document. While it may be easy during the research stage to keep all relevant information coordinated, as a process moves further into its life cycle the information coordination process becomes more complex. Creating a group responsible for the development of each specific technology and conducting periodic technology audits are two techniques that have been used to facilitate the maintenance of good documentation.

Another issue related to organizing the process definition documentation management system involves assigning responsibility for reviewing and endorsing the process on behalf of the firm. As the process documentation is being prepared, it should serve as a guide for the firm in the design and conduct of the process. Someone, often the senior engineering and senior research and development officers, should indicate acceptance of the technology as it evolves during the design process.

Appropriate skills must be made available during the development of process documentation. For example, all the process engineers, chemists, and health and safety specialists should be involved. These staff members should have access to appropriate information sources, including internal personnel who have operated and designed the process in question (or related processes), process licensors, engineering contractors, reference materials, and on-line data bases that include hazard and engineering information.

The management system for process definition documentation should assure that the contents of the process documentation package are accurate and complete. A suitable review and quality assurance program should be implemented for the process documentation. This may involve a hierarchical review process, and/or using external experts in a review capacity. Reference 64 describes a process documentation system that is based on strict process discipline.

There are several control issues involved in developing and maintaining process definition documentation. First, there should be a mechanism for keeping track of the dissemination of copies of the documentation (e.g., a system for numbering copies). This is important to assure that changes and updates are distributed to all affected parties so that no one is working from obsolete information. Second, there should be a review process for changes to assure that changes to process documentation receive the same degree of scrutiny that was applied to the original documentation package.

4.4 Process and Equipment Design

Documenting process and equipment design has long-term importance for process safety. For example, the design specifications for process equipment may be needed in the future for the engineering of new capital projects, and the piping and instrumentation drawings (P&IDs) will be needed to support hazard studies. Consequently, a method for archiving plant design information is clearly a need that must be met.

Examples of the type of process and equipment design information that should be compiled is shown in Table 4-3. In general, the documentation should include any information needed to verify design conditions, size, materials of construction, failure modes of controls, piping, and instrumentation in the plant. A detailed listing of appropriate project documentation can be found in Lee's Loss Prevention in the Process Industries. (Reference 49)

Table 4-3
Examples of Process and Equipment Design Information

- Process flow diagrams
- Design energy and mass balances
- Plot plan with electrical classifications
- Plot plan showing underground/fire water piping
- Piping and instrumentation drawings
- Equipment process/mechanical data sheets
- Equipment catalogs
- Valve and instrumentation data sheets (especially pressure relief systems)
- Piping specification
- CAD files
- Electrical one-line drawings
- Control system description
- Vendor operation and maintenance manuals
- Computer-controlled plant hardware and software

The process and equipment documentation management systems should assure that all original documents (design drawings, equipment specifications, computer programs, scale-up documentation, etc.) are archived in a retrievable manner and responsibility for assuring that this information is retained should be assigned. For example, everyone involved in the design process should be required to submit materials to the designated "archivist". The archivist, in turn, should develop checklists of expected project documentation so that follow-up can be initiated when items are not submitted.

During the startup and operating life of a facility, as changes are made to equipment, a paper trail should be generated and managed to permit determination of both the current status of the equipment, and how it evolved from the original design. To initiate this paper trail, management systems are required that will cause several areas of activity in the plant, such as maintenance, operations, and technical services, to interact.

A large number of modifications to processes occur through simple maintenance tasks. Although most of this activity involves "like-for-like" replacement of equipment, there are occasions when non-identical changes may occur. This may result from the lack of availability of an exact duplicate part, or the need for temporary bypassing, or a trial run of a new product or process change. Such modifications should be addressed through management of change procedures (see Chapter 7). The maintenance work order system should provide for capture of the relevant documentation.

Where a major equipment change is involved (e.g., in modernizing a plant), the process and equipment documentation systems should capture the required design documentation from the process engineering staff or other departments. This is a variation of the new process documentation system described above.

The process and equipment documentation management systems should facilitate the transfer of technology among locations within the firm. Often a new location, or a new unit at an existing location, will incorporate new equipment designs. As these designs are proven effective, there may be opportunities for upgrading throughout the firm. The use of "engineering councils", which bring together engineers and other technical personnel from throughout a firm to discuss common opportunities and issues, can provide a mechanism for sharing information on new equipment.

Documentation of the process and equipment should also be used in training both operating and maintenance personnel. Understanding the capabilities and limitations of equipment and the basis for selection of specific types of equipment or materials of construction helps make operators and maintenance personnel better able to monitor safety. Operators and maintenance staff, in turn, can help improve the quality of the documentation by assuring that the documentation and the actual plant conditions are consistent with each other.

4.5 Protective Systems

Protective systems designed to mitigate risks are a special category of process equipment. Examples of protective systems are shown in Table 4-4. The management of protective systems information should occur within the management of systems for process and equipment, as discussed in the previous section. However, with protective systems equipment, it is particularly important to record and disseminate information on promising new approaches, and on problems with older approaches.

Some protective systems may be shared across a site, providing protection to more than one unit. Their documentation may be maintained separately from documentation of individual units, but should be available to operators and supervisors in each affected unit.

Documentation of protective systems should clearly indicate the design basis of each system. The rationale for arriving at the design basis should also be documented.

4.6 Normal and Upset Conditions (Operating Procedures)

Documentation of normal operating conditions involves the development of operating procedures. These procedures are useful in operator training and in guiding the operator in day-to-day tasks. Operating procedures describe the tasks to be performed by the operator, instrument readings data to be collected, samples to be taken, and operating conditions (e.g., temperature, pressure, material addition rate, etc.) to be maintained. The operating procedures also indicate safety precautions to be taken during the operation.

In the course of operation, all process plants will experience upsets because of control malfunction, pump outage, power outage, and the like. During such upsets, process conditions may deviate from the normal operating range. It is important that operators know the safe operating limits for critical operating parameters for hazardous operations. These should be established and incorporated into the operating procedures.

Further documentation of critical operating parameters and critical instruments is desirable. The documentation of critical operating procedures and instruments can help focus training attention on assuring that the operator thoroughly understands the implications of operating outside allowable limits. This documentation can also serve

Table 4-4
Examples of Protective Systems
(and related design issues)

---

1. Pressure Relief/Vent Collection
- Safety valve redundancy
- Sizing for multiple contingencies
- Use of automatic depressurization valves
- Cold, warm, toxic, and corrosive vapor collection headers, including segregation, temperature limits, materials of construction, piping spec. changes, knock-out drums, and the like.

2. Release Devices (flares, scrubbers, etc.)
- Atmospheric vs. controlled releases
- Elevated and ground flares
- Scrubber/incinerator requirements, reliability, by-passing
- Monitoring devices (thermocouples, analyzers)

3. Plant/Equipment Isolation
- Remote isolation capability
- Isolation valve performance (acid/fire-rated, quick closure, emergency power, and such)
- Valve location (pump suction, under vessels with a large inventory of hazardous materials)
- Location of pushbuttons

4. Critical Alarms/Interlocks
- Independent sensor/switches
- Redundancy of signals, voting
- Hardware vs. software

5. Fire Detection/Protection
- Flame/smoke detectors
- Water system (mains, hydrants/monitors, nozzles, emergency supply)
- Deluge/spray systems (application to pumps/vessels, nozzle-type, activation)
- Foam systems (fix, portable, foam-type)

6. Gas Detection
- Combustible, toxic, specie-specific
- Location, elevation

7. Emergency System Services
- Back-up power, instrument air
- Uninterruptible power supply

---

as a useful quick reference during upset conditions. It also alerts the maintenance staff to instruments that require regular checking to ensure proper operation. The documentation of critical operating parameters should identify these parameters by reference to control instrumentation and alarms. It should also discuss the safety concern of operating beyond the safe limits of the critical operating parameters. The distinction between alarm levels (warning vs. action alarms) needs to be addressed as well. Finally, a discussion of corrective and emergency actions that are needed to prevent a hazardous situation from escalating should be provided. This type of narrative should be prepared individually for each process step where critical operating parameters or critical instruments are involved.

Plants that employ computerized process control systems introduce additional complexity to the documentation of operating procedures. The computer control system interacts directly with the process in ways that may or may not be apparent to the operator. In such plants, the operating procedures should describe the linkages between the control system and the process, as well as the logic built into the software.

Operating procedures should include input from both process and design engineers as well as operations personnel (including operators). Effective operating procedures are technically accurate while also being clearly understandable to the operator. They should also reflect the practical consideration of how operations are actually carried out.

Each operating procedure should have a date and/or revision number on every page, as well as the process name and plant location, to assist in tracking changes. The operating procedures should be updated whenever there is an equipment, procedural, or software change so that the procedures always reflect the intended operating practice. The management system should assure that procedures are updated as needed, and that all users are informed whenever there is a change. The original operating procedure, as well as all subsequent changes, should be approved by responsible management as specified by the management system (e.g., the manager responsible for the operation).

Responsibility for identifying critical operating procedures should include the process engineering and process chemistry staff and operating personnel. The production staff should be accountable for assuring that all operators are familiar with critical operating procedures. As a result, the documentation of critical operating procedures for operator use is best done by operating personnel, and it should reflect their language and their familiarity with process control systems.

The selection of critical operating parameters should be reviewed and updated at regular intervals (e.g., every three years). Intermediate updates may be appropriate based upon newly discovered information or an accident/incident situation that occurred. Changes to critical operating parameters should be made only after careful review and approval through a mechanism established by the management system. All changes must be thoroughly documented.

4.7 Process Risk Management Decisions

During the course of chemical plant design and operation, certain actions are taken to reduce the risk of hazardous material releases and exposure. Technical evaluation of options and consequence and risk analyses may be prepared. The analyses might include calculation of credible release quantities of hazardous materials and subsequent dispersion model results to estimate impact zones. Subsequently, the basis for a mitigation system may be generated. This might involve, for example, a secondary containment structure, explosion suppression system, or scrubber. The rationale and technical design basis for such decisions should be documented and retained as part of the process knowledge.

The management system for documentation of process risk management decisions must address the sensitive issue of legal liability. The law departments of some firms believe that documentation of risk analysis, wherein the firm acknowledges the possibility of accidents, creates unacceptable liabilities. Many other attorneys see this as an important exercise in demonstrating the firm's affirmative action in trying to understand and manage risks. The management system for risk management decision documentation should be carefully coordinated with the firm's attorneys, who are likely to have concerns over such issues as confidentiality, use of incriminating and inflammatory language, documentation of mitigation measures, and record retention.

The management system for process risk management decisions must be designed to capture information that describes not only what decision was made but also why it was made. This can be important in explaining differences among plants within a single firm. However, there are not always rigorous systems for capturing the "why" information. Accordingly, the management system for process risk management decision documentation should enlist the cooperation of individuals throughout both the safety and the capital expenditure approval chains. This management system should be designed to receive every safety analysis as well as every capital project request designated as a safety-related project. With these as triggers, the system should prompt the completion of a complete "chain of thought" regarding risk; e.g., what initiated the study (or request), what was recommended and why, was it accepted and, if not, why, and was it implemented?

4.8 Company Memory (Management of Information)

Knowledge and information obtained from plant experience and mistakes frequently result in enhanced operations. In other words, plants often settle on a way of conducting an operation as a result of practical experience. However, if the reason for having adopted this practice is not documented, later generations of supervisors may resurrect ineffective alternatives, not knowing that they have already been tried.

The process and equipment documentation, as well as the operating and upset procedures, should create an archival history of the operation. In addition, while it is important to know the current status of the operation, it is also important to be able to look back and learn from the operation's history to improve process safety continuously.

Retention of historical information must be done in accordance with the firm's record retention policy, where one exists. However, in all cases, it is important to think in terms of when the information will be needed, not simply when it was created.

There should be specific responsibility assigned for the maintenance of historical records. Issues of importance, which should be addressed by the management system, include specifying who will keep the records, where and how they will be maintained, and how they can be retrieved and used at both the facility and company-wide levels.

In addition, there should be adequate consideration for backing-up critical records and protecting the records against loss.

An important aspect of the company memory is the knowledge and experience possessed by senior operators, supervisors, and engineers. Over the years, many things happen in a plant that are not written down, but the ability to relate new questions or problems to past experience is critical to effective problem-solving. This experience is usually passed on from older to younger workers over time. However, when downsizing or streamlining programs results in many of these experienced people leaving an organization at once (e.g., to take advantage of early retirement incentives), a gap in the company memory can be created. Should such situations threaten to arise, the process knowledge management system should prompt the initiation of programs to capture as much experience-based information as possible. This might involve such activities as engaging early retirees temporarily as consultants, or undertaking organized "debriefing" sessions. The use of "knowledge engineering" techniques, now employed in developing expert systems, provides a structured way to capture this information.

5

Process Safety Review Procedures for Capital Projects

5.1 Overview

Capital projects may involve the construction of complete plants in the case of major capacity additions or the manufacture of new products. Capital projects may also involve substantial facilities modifications in the case of alterations to existing facilities. Since such projects involve many types of changes (e.g., new equipment, new chemistries, state-of-the-art controls, new operating procedures, increases in chemical inventories, etc.), the need for some level of "process safety review" has been a recognized feature of in-house and contract project engineering organizations. Such process safety reviews typically address such things as equipment overpressure protection (e.g., pressure relief system design), materials of construction, fire protection systems, and maintainability.

With the public's heightened awareness of chemical hazards and more stringent federal and state government regulation of the chemical industry, project reviews need to be comprehensive and systematic. Not only do all process hazards need to be identified and addressed by the design, but broader issues need to be considered and premises challenged. For example, such questions as the following need to be answered:

- Is the company prepared to accept the inherent hazards and potential risks of this project?
- Is the location appropriate for the types of operations envisioned?

Also new and more effective techniques have been used increasingly for the evaluation of traditionally recognized issues, such as:

- Has the chemistry been thoroughly investigated such that all process hazards are known?
- Does the design adequately address all the process hazards?
- Have the equipment, piping, and controls instrumentation been checked for inadvertently "designed-in" hazards?

- Does the installed equipment conform to the design, as delineated by the drawings and specifications?
- Have computer systems been adequately checked and documented?
- Are the consequences of process deviations known, and are the consequences acceptable?
- Does the design address the possibility of human failure, and does it adequately handle the consequences of such failures?

To adequately protect the company from the possibility of a major loss or liability, project review procedures need to be formalized and documented to obtain the quality and management control that are commensurate with the risk. Communication of the results of the various reviews to appropriate levels of management is also essential to tap "collective knowledge" and capture various organizational perspectives. Reviews also need to be done in early stages of the project to avoid costly modifications later on. The most cost-effective loss prevention takes place in these early stages of the project.

This chapter provides guidelines for comprehensive project review process safety management systems, beginning with process development and concluding with the initiation of routine production after startup. The Guidelines presented here should be integrated with those of Chapter 4 (Documentation), Chapter 7 (Management of Change), and Chapter 6 (Process Risk Management) in an all-inclusive process safety review approach.

The process safety management element entitled "Capital Projects Design Review Procedures" addresses the need for assuring that equipment and construction are properly reviewed when making physical (hardware) changes. These review procedures are important for any change that could affect process safety, regardless of the cost of making the change. Thus, changes that might be too small in cost to be considered in a firm's capital expenditure financial review process may, nonetheless, be of interest for process safety review.

Process safety review procedures should interact with a project from its inception through its completion. One way of depicting the phases of a project is shown in Figure 5-1. This model identifies five phases of a typical major capital project:

- Phase I -- Conceptual Engineering -- involves the technical and economic evaluation of a project's feasibility, including process chemistry, process hazards, flow schematics, fundamental design basis for equipment, instruments and controls, and safety systems.

- Phase II -- Basic Engineering -- involves process simulation calculations (mass and energy balances) and process flow design (PFD), concluding with piping and instrumentation diagrams (P&IDs), and equipment data sheets issued for design.

- Phase III -- Detail Design -- involves vessel thickness calculations, exchanger rating, line sizing and piping design, and isometric drawings, concluding with specifications and drawings issued for construction.

- Phase IV -- Equipment Procurement and Construction -- involves purchasing of fabricated and bulk materials and installation on site.

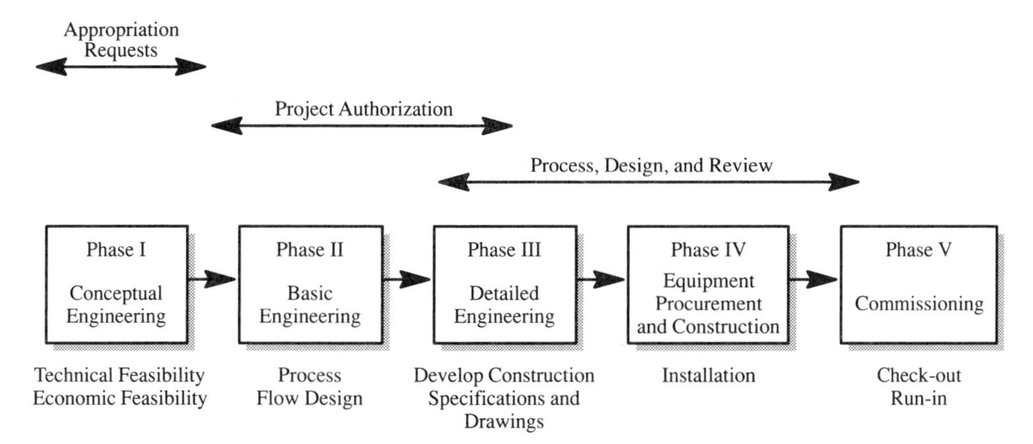

Figure 5–1. *The Phases of a Capital Project*

- Phase V -- Commissioning Prior to Startup -- involves check-out and run-in activities performed to ensure that equipment and piping are mechanically integrated and free of obstructions, seeing that instruments and controls are functioning properly, and a check of any other aspect of the project that should be monitored for safe and effective operation.

Process safety considerations should begin during Phase I, with input to the project scope of work and conceptual cost estimate on process safety-related needs and costs. As the project design is refined, process safety considerations should become increasingly detailed. As the project moves through construction and checkout, process safety input should shift to confirmation and verification.

These project phases are not always scheduled sequentially and they often overlap. This is particularly true on so-called "fast-track" projects where schedules are intentionally compressed. Also, for well-established process technologies, Phases I and II are sometimes combined. Effective coordination of review procedures during the different project phases is crucial to effective quality assurance and the ability to effect improvements in the design. Fast-track projects must not be allowed to short-cut process safety review procedures.

Process safety management systems for capital project design review procedures must consider a number of components:

- Appropriation request procedures,
- Hazard reviews,
- Siting,
- Plot plans,
- Process design and review procedures, and
- Project management procedures and controls.

Each of these components is discussed below.

5.2 Appropriation Request Procedures

At the earliest stages of a capital project, a scope of work and associated cost estimate for the project should be developed. These are used to obtain initial approvals for development work, and serve to guide the early engineering stages of the project. The process safety management system should assure that the scope and initial cost estimate reflect process safety requirements. Consideration of these issues at the formative stages of a project can help assure that financial and engineering provisions are made for special process safety issues. One way to assure consideration of these issues is to require inclusion of a process safety section in the scope of work document.

Should the Phase I feasibility study indicate an economically viable project, then the financial and business management systems would typically require preparation of a project justification at the early planning stages to support the appropriation request. For large projects, there are usually two stages of authorization: one for initiating basic engineering and another for approval of detailed design and construction. This documentation may be the first detailed project assessment seen by the business managers, and is a key input to their decisions on whether the project is consistent with the firm's business plans.

The process safety management system should be integrated with the planning process and the funding authorization systems to assure that process safety is considered from the outset of the project. This can be accomplished by assuring that all appropriation requests address both the rewards of the proposed project and the risks, including the potential for chemical release and exposure, environmental damage, and asset loss. The requests should then present the methods recommended for managing the process risks identified, and include estimated levels of resources required for management or control of the process risks.

In organizing an appropriation request review system, senior management responsible for approving expenditures will require that process safety considerations be addressed. Assignment of authority for approval of appropriation requests should be clear, with explicit understanding that approval indicates acceptance of the process safety evaluation inherent in the request. It is important to perform the process safety risk evaluation at the appropriation request stage using personnel with appropriate backgrounds. Process engineers, research staff, and operations personnel all have important contributions to make to the evaluation. It may be appropriate and desirable to have this section of the request document reviewed by an "outsider" to ensure that safety, health, environmental, and loss prevention aspects have been objectively presented.

The appropriation request or supporting documentation should have a section that discusses the chemical and process hazards of the materials being handled, stored, used and produced. Prior to completing this section, the originator of the request should consider the following questions:

- What are the toxic, flammable, and reactive chemicals involved, and, what is the hazardous nature of each of these materials?
- What is the estimated on-site inventory of each chemical that will be required?
- What are the major or worst-case release scenarios, including impact/loss potential of each (e.g., personnel exposure to toxic materials, environmental impact, liability, business interruption)?

- How does the estimated process risk compare to other existing or proposed operations?
- How are the risks from this process going to be controlled?

All managers (including business managers) with final authority for approving appropriation requests should make completion of the hazard definition a prerequisite for approval. They should also be expected to understand the nature and magnitude of the risks described, and accept these risks through their appropriation approval. Where the risks are substantial in magnitude, the decision to proceed should be made at the management level appropriate to consideration of such risks.

Different levels of hazard review and risk assessment will be necessary, depending upon the nature of the potential impacts caused by loss of process control and/or containment. The management system should include provisions for assuring that requests involving potentially major risks receive a more comprehensive review than other requests. This may be done through the establishment of threshold criteria based on chemical use (e.g., involves more than a given amount of a highly toxic material), or using a scoring index (e.g., exceeds a given value on the Dow index), or having a safety professional subjectively judge each request.

Implementation of effective appropriation reviews is simplified when the appropriation request document indicates what issues are to be considered, and what types of analysis are to be done (e.g., checklist, what if, HAZOP, fault tree). Unambiguous criteria should be provided for determining when such assessments are needed.

The major control issue in making a process safety review of appropriation requests is assuring that an adequate review is done for every project. The integrity of the review process can be compromised by the temptation to bypass reviews during "fast-track" projects, or the making of assumptions about process and materials hazards in the absence of valid information. A common way to use accountability as a means of control is to require the engineer originating a project, and each manager who reviews it, to explicitly sign off on their consideration of and acceptance of the process safety aspects of the project. The explicit identification of a project as being "fast track" may be done in an effort to expedite reviews, but this designation should prompt increased concern for ensuring that the safety review process is complete and is based on the needed information.

A common approach employed in fast-track projects is to move forward using available information rather than waiting for information gaps to be filled prior to proceeding. In such cases, a tracking and monitoring system is needed to be sure that data gaps are filled, and that the data obtained results in reconsideration of earlier decisions, before finalizing the design. Expediting a project by moving forward before data gaps are filled involves assuming a financial risk, since work will proceed based on assumptions regarding how the gaps will be filled. However, the assumption of this financial risk must not permit the relaxation of control of process risks.

5.3 Siting

In planning a project, site-selection decisions should take into account the risk of exposing human populations to the hazards of toxic and flammable chemicals.

Therefore, in the evaluation of sites, the consequences of "credible worst case" scenarios need to be considered. Examples of events that could involve a major loss of inventory include: line failure, blow out of a reactor rupture disk or gasket, or a spill during tank car transfer, and in some cases vessel failure. (Transportation issues are excluded from the scope of this document, but should also be considered in siting.)

Good project planning dictates that alternative sites be considered at project inception. This ensures that there are backup options in the event that the siting review finds the primary site presents too much exposure. The siting analysis and review should be done during the conceptual or basic engineering phase, before a large commitment has been made to a specific site location. In this way, a decision to relocate the plant can be made without major cost and schedule implications, which can be very compelling arguments for staying put.

The management system for site selection should be organized to designate accountability for explicitly making the siting decision, rather than having it occur by default. It can be helpful to have a checklist of siting considerations for use by decision-makers. Table 5-1 provides an example of such a list.

The process safety management system should provide guidance in determining which risks to consider during site selection. The management system should help assure that decisions are based on reasonable and consistent assumptions. For example, in evaluating the impact of toxic vapor release scenarios, it may not be reasonable to assume that all the released material becomes airborne. The physical conditions of the released material, the ambient temperature and wind conditions, and spill containment provisions will all affect estimates of vapor generation used to estimate potential off-site impacts. Unrealistic assumptions can result in presenting the site selection decision-maker with misleading information.

Siting situations may occur where potential offsite impacts involving the general public cannot be avoided. In such cases, the process safety management system should prompt consideration of how potential public impact can be minimized. Such alternatives as inventory reduction or changing processes to change the intermediates in storage may be considered.

In some selected situations, a more definitive approach may be appropriate, e.g., quantifying the total site risk by evaluating the consequences and probability (i.e., risk)

Table 5-1
Example Checklist of Process Safety Siting Considerations

- Is there an adequate buffer zone between the operation and vulnerable populations and public facilities (e.g., homes, schools, hospitals)?
- Is there good transportation into the site for raw materials and product?
- Is there adequate water supply for fire protection?
- Is there suitable emergency response support (e.g., medical resources) in nearby communities?
- Are there nearby sources of risk that could threaten the site?
- Is the location subject to weather extremes (e.g., earthquake, hurricanes)?
- Are there topographic features that could increase the effect of a chemical release?

of all credible release events. This can be done by applying quantitative risk analysis techniques described in the AIChE/CCPS publication, Guidelines for Chemical Process Quantitative Risk Analysis.

As a control to assure adequate process safety evaluation, the site selection decision-maker should require a written assessment before making a decision.

5.4 Plot Plan

The engineering design of a project should be guided from the early planning stages by the process safety goals of the company. Some companies have extensive engineering standards and process safety considerations integrated throughout their standards. Other firms have separate process safety design guidelines that address issues such as the location of storage tanks.

In implementing a capital project, design standards inherently influence the level of process risk that will be acceptable. For example, the arrangement of process equipment, storage vessels, and buildings will be influenced by requirements for safe distances from onsite and offsite populated areas. For flammable materials, consideration should be given to established guidelines (e.g., NFPA-30) for separation distances for storage vessels. In addition, the National Electrical Code (NFPA-70) provides guidelines for electrical safety in areas where flammables and combustibles are present. In the case of toxic materials, there are no established codes for separation and placement of storage containers. Guidelines for plot plan arrangement of toxic materials storage areas can be found in several other CCPS publications (References 32,48,73). Process safety management systems for guidelines and standards are discussed in Chapter 12.

The process safety management system should require that site layout be reviewed specifically for conformance to risk-reduction guidelines. Subsequent changes to the plot plan (from expansions, rearrangements, or removal of operations) should be similarly reviewed. The management system should identify a procedure for initiating these reviews, define responsibility for the conduct of the reviews, and provide a mechanism for problem resolution.

Safe layout requires input from staff familiar with the site (and existing operations), as well as from those with specialized knowledge of process hazards and protection systems. For example, input may be needed from fire protection engineers, electrical engineers, and process engineers. The design process organization should allow for such input.

5.5 Hazard Reviews

The purpose of a hazard review during the life cycle of a capital project is to effectively identify any hazard so that control measures can be developed in subsequent efforts (either by the same staff or by others). Hazard reviews use an organized, systematic approach that includes documentation of results. Corporate policies and procedures should require hazard reviews in conjunction with any project that has potential process safety implications. The hazard identification team should check all

Table 5-2
Hazard Review Procedures

Steps in Hazard Evaluation Process	Hazard Evaluation Procedures: Process/System Checklists	Safety Review	Relative Ranking Dow & Mond	Preliminary Hazard Analysis	"What If" Method	Hazard and Operability Study	Failure Modes Effects and Criticality Analysis	Fault Tree Analysis	Event Tree Analysis	Cause Consequence Analysis	Human Error Analysis
Identify Deviations From Good Practice	Primary Purpose	Primary Purpose	Primary Purpose								
Identify Hazards	Primary Purpose*	Primary Purpose*	Primary Purpose*	Primary Purpose	Primary Purpose	Primary Purpose	Primary Purpose	Provides Context Only			
Estimate "Worst Case" Consequences			Primary Purpose		Primary Purpose	Provides Context Only	Primary Purpose				
Identify Opportunities to Reduce Consequences			Primary Purpose	Secondary Purpose		Provides Context Only	Provides Context Only				
Identify Accident Initiating Events					Primary Purpose	Primary Purpose	Primary Purpose	Primary Purpose			Primary Purpose
Estimate Probabilities of Initiating Events						Provides Context Only	Provides Context Only	Primary Purpose		Primary Purpose	Primary Purpose
Identify Opportunities to Reduce Probabilities of Initiating Events								Primary Purpose		Primary Purpose	Primary Purpose
Identify Accident Event Sequences and Consequences					Primary Purpose			Primary Purpose	Primary Purpose	Primary Purpose	
Estimate Probabilities of Event Sequences								Primary Purpose	Primary Purpose	Primary Purpose	
Estimate Magnitude of Consequences of Event Sequences									Provides Context Only	Provides Context Only	
Identify Opportunities to Reduce Probabilities and/or Consequences of Event Sequences									Primary Purpose	Primary Purpose	Primary Purpose
Quantitative Hazard Evaluation								Primary Purpose	Primary Purpose	Primary Purpose	Primary Purpose

* Previously Recognized Hazards Only.

control measures to assure that all issues have been addressed and that the control measures adopted have effectively addressed the hazards.

A series of process hazard reviews should be performed at various stages of a capital project, commencing with the earliest conceptual consideration. At this early stage, which is often simply an exploration of possible direction, driven by business requirements or opportunities, process hazard issues should be considered in a general way to rule out further work on proposals with clearly unacceptable risks. The process safety management system should provide resources to managers involved in this early business planning so that they can factor process safety into their thinking.

Additional process hazard reviews should then occur as the project progresses, with the level of sophistication and detail of the review increasing, along with the development of project details. Several types of hazard review procedures are available and can be applied in project reviews. These are listed in Table 5-2. More information on the practice and implementation of these techniques can be found in References 12,24,48,63.

As Figure 5-2 depicts, the information available to the hazard review process varies with the stages of the project. Since the hazard review techniques in Table 5-2 require different degrees of detailed information, their applicability depends on the stage of the project. For example, a failure modes and effects analysis is hardware-specific and should not be considered until the detailed design stage when equipment specifications are available. The hazard review management system should assure that an appropriate review technique is used at each stage of the project.

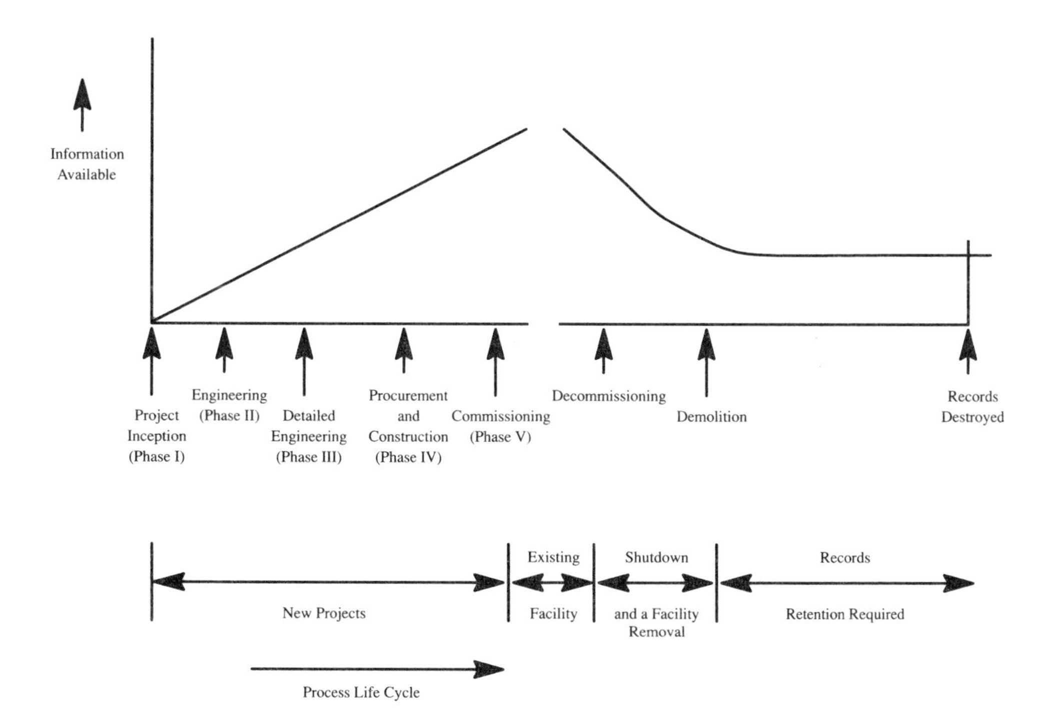

Figure 5–2. *Information Available to Hazard Review*

Organizing the hazard review should provide for assembling a multi-disciplinary team, drawing on the various functional parts of the organization. Some firms include personnel not directly involved in the project to maintain objectivity. Different review techniques require staffing different skills, with the following functions and skills typically represented on the team:

- Process engineering (project),
- Manufacturing (operations),
- Research and development,
- Maintenance,
- Environmental control,
- Safety and loss prevention,
- Design specialties (as needed).

Staff assigned to the review should possess sufficient experience to contribute to a thorough exploration of potential hazards.

The hazards review process needs to be documented effectively:

- Describe and communicate the hazards identified,
- List recommendations to control hazards,
- Retain and track unanswered questions,
- Provide a basis for subsequent analysis.

The documentation of the hazard review provides a control mechanism by showing what evaluation was done, and allowing follow-up to assure that subsequent changes were made where appropriate. Where it is decided not to implement mitigation measures, documentation should describe the considerations involved and the basis for the decision.

A running checklist of hazard review recommendations and followup items, indicating responsibility and status, should be issued and updated by the hazard review team leader. All outstanding items must be resolved in subsequent project phases--and definitely prior to startup. This is particularly important for procedural recommendations that can get overshadowed by design considerations. Procedural recommendations should be incorporated into the operating manual and standard operating procedures before commissioning the plant. The management system should involve clear assignment of responsibility for assuring that all hazard review recommendations have been implemented consistent with designated timing, and that required actions have been verified at the outset of the commissioning process.

5.6 Process Design and Review Procedures

Major capital projects should--and typically do--include an informal review or checking of design details by design specialists. Cross-checking information on vendor drawings against the equipment specifications is an example of such a review. However, the design procedures should also incorporate formal reviews by the core design team to provide quality control on the project design. Essential reviews that should be required for each project are process safety design review(s) and the pre-startup safety survey.

The appropriate times to perform design reviews will vary among projects. When reviews are done earlier in the design process, resulting changes to the design are easier to make; however, the amount of design information available may be limited. When the reviews are performed later, there is more information available; however, it may be more difficult and costly to make changes.

One of the key transition points in the project occurs near the end of basic engineering (Phase II) when drawings and specifications are issued for "design" (detailed engineering). This is the appropriate time for conducting process safety reviews. These are methodical reviews to verify the integrity of the equipment and piping for the anticipated range of operating conditions, and to check the adequacy of alarms and interlocks that are protecting against operation outside of design limits. Items typically covered in these reviews are listed in Table 5-3.

Another critical transfer point is at the end of the plant construction (Phase IV), when the equipment is being readied for startup. On large projects, this is usually a formal phase called commissioning (Phase V), which involves pre-startup activities. Pre-startup activities generally begin before all construction activities have been completed, and involve making sure the plant is mechanically complete and free of debris. At this point, a pre-startup safety survey should be initiated. The purpose of this survey is to ensure that all elements of process safety, including hardware, procedures, and control software, are in place prior to startup, and that all prior issues of concern have been resolved.

A pre-startup safety survey should be guided by a checklist to help assure thorough implementation. Examples of the subjects typically covered by a pre-startup safety survey checklist are given in Table 5-4.

Table 5-3
Examples of Issues Typically Covered in a Design Stage Process Safety Review

- Equipment design temperature/pressure vs. process conditions
- Pressure-relief device sizing criteria and location
- Control valve "fail-safe" mode
- Set points of emergency alarms, trips, and interlocks
- Reactive chemical considerations
- Backup provisions for utilities and services
- Computer programs
- Conformance with electrical classifications
- Critical instruments
- Fire protection and vapor suppression system design
- Vent header/flare system sizing criteria and compatibility of pressure-relief device tie-ins
- Compatibility of materials of construction
- Line sizing and specification

Table 5-4
Example of a Pre-Startup Safety Review Checklist

- Have all hazard review recommendations been addressed?
- Has the safety critical equipment list been prepared?
- Have all the safety critical equipment been properly installed and are they functional?
- Have the operating manuals been completed and approved?
- Have standard operating procedures been written, including startup and shutdown?
- Have the operators and maintenance personnel received orientation on the process and health hazards of the plant?
- Have the operators been sufficiently trained in the operating procedures for the plant?
- Are field change authorization procedures in place?
- Has all computer control logic been thoroughly tested?
- Has an emergency response organization been assembled and have responsibilities been assigned?
- Has a written emergency response plan been prepared, and have practice drills been run?

The safety management system should tie into the project tracking system to assure that the safety reviews are initiated at the appropriate time. The results of these reviews should be documented, and there should be clearly defined accountability for assuring implementation of recommendations from the hazard review. The design process should include controls that assure the completion of the required reviews before the project moves on to the next step. Where a formal project management tracking system is employed, resolution of safety review items can become work tasks whose completion is required before initiation of later tasks. Where less formal project management approaches are used or smaller projects are involved, design engineers might be asked to document (through memos) their approaches to the resolution of safety concerns.

Process hazard reviews should not be overlooked in cases where design has been performed by a vendor (e.g., in cases of turnkey plants or purchased technologies). The technology buyer's policies and procedures should require that process hazard reviews be performed by the vendor, and they may specify the review procedures to be used. As an alternative, or as an additional review, the firm's personnel or a third-party consultant may be used to perform the review. An independent review may be performed separate from the vendor's review, or the independent personnel may participate with vendor personnel in a joint review. Making these reviews a contractual requirement can be an effective management control mechanism.

5.7 Project Management Procedures and Controls

Project management procedures and controls are also an essential part of process safety management, especially for extending quality assurance to the fabrication and installation of equipment. At this stage of a project, the key role of the process safety management system is the control function of assuring that plans are carried out as intended. In this context, quality assurance efforts should focus on ensuring that process equipment is fabricated in accordance with design specifications, assembled and installed properly, and that the maintenance organization has the required information to maintain the original level of integrity.

The quality assurance effort begun in the preceding project phases should continue into the vendor's facility where critical service equipment is involved. This activity is sometimes referred to as non-process quality control. It often begins with prequalification of vendors who will be involved in fabrication of critical service equipment. An example is the screening of pipe spool fabricators to assess their quality control and certification procedures on jobs utilizing fine-grain, impact-tested carbon steel.

It is hardly necessary to stress the importance of plant inspection during the fabrication, construction, and commissioning of process facilities. An inspection system and the presence of inspectors have a significant influence on the quality of the work done. During fabrication, inspectors can and should be used to confirm assembly aspects such as:

- Proper materials of contruction,
- Proper use of welding techniques,
- Employment of qualified welders,
- Verification of correct dimensions.

Another aspect of non-process quality control should focus on bulk materials used in the construction of the plant. This includes items such as pipes and fittings, valves, gaskets, welding rods, and the like. Warehouse procedures for proper labeling and segregation by type of material are an important control procedure where hazardous materials are to be processed. In situations where there are a number of different piping specifications involved, some in critical service, a materials-positive identification procedure for testing items at receiving will be required. Piping failures have occurred because a length of plain carbon steel pipe was unknowingly substituted for "killed" carbon steel in low-temperature service. Strong testing and labeling systems (e.g., painting a color code on tested materials suitable for a particular type of service) can help avoid such incidents.

When a project involves higher than normal risks, or is under close scrutiny by government regulators and the general public, the use of inspection specialists in the form of consultants can be of benefit. Consultants (who may come from outside the firm or from a specialist staff group within the firm) provide the opportunity for an organization to improve or enhance its process safety management in the area of mechanical integrity. Consultants can be a valuable resource to the construction supervision organization by acting as independent auditors/inspectors during the installation of equipment, piping, and instrumentation. The use of consultants specializing in a particular field helps ensure that a wide range of possible solutions, including latest technology, is considered.

In concluding this section, it needs to be mentioned that it is all too easy for these procedures and controls to be de-emphasized or ignored in striving to control project costs and schedule. To ensure against this situation, these activities should be made part of the project scope, including schedule allotment and appropriate budget allocation. The intent is to achieve effective quality control, rather than to reduce the process to a reporting exercise.

6
Process Risk Management

6.1 Overview

Process risk management involves the systematic identification, evaluation, and control of potential losses that may arise in existing operating facilities from future events such as fires, explosions, toxic releases, runaway reactions, or natural disasters. Whether resulting losses are measured in terms of direct costs, impacts on employees and/or the public, property and/or environmental damage, lost business, penalties, or liabilities, the possibility of experiencing such losses is considered a risk. Even when effective capital project review systems have been used to "design out" many risks, there will still be a residual risk. Corporate managers must inevitably face these residual risks in dealing successfully with the everyday operation of their businesses and with the long-term planning of new ventures.

The practice of process risk management anticipates the possibility of process safety-related losses and evaluates their potential impacts so they can be managed effectively. Process risk management requires recognition of possible risks, evaluation of the likelihood of hazardous events, the magnitude of their consequences, and determination of appropriate measures for reduction of these risks. Thus, process risk management is a practical instrument that can assist in business decision-making in the face of uncertainty.

A company should put in place management systems that will assure appropriate process risk management. These systems might include review and approval programs, risk acceptability guidelines, business-area risk reviews, pre-acquisition risk reviews, and residual risk management.

Once a corporation has adopted the techniques of process risk management in the conduct of its business, there are numerous benefits to be gained. Anticipation and prevention of potential failures within a facility can reduce downtime and the resulting loss of revenue associated with business interruption. Risk analysis also allows the evaluation of existing process safety measures, and can point out areas for improvement in a facility's overall process safety design and operating procedures. Results of risk analyses are also important in planning effective emergency response procedures.

A process risk management program must be capable of addressing the full range of hazards associated with a diverse set of operations. This chapter outlines the components of such a program, specifically:

- Hazard identification,
- Risk analysis of operations,
- Reduction of risk,
- Residual risk management,
- Process management during emergencies,
- Encouraging client and supplier companies to adopt similar risk management practices, and
- Selection of businesses with acceptable risk.

6.2 Hazard Identification

Hazard identification is the process of determining what hazards are associated with a given operation or design, as it is operating. In existing operations, hazard identification is performed periodically to determine the implications of changes to process knowledge, and new guidelines and standards, and to recognize changes to processes, procedures, equipment, and materials.

The role of hazard identification in process risk management at existing operations is to establish the foundation upon which many of the other process safety management components build. The following point is important to recognize:

If hazards are not identified, they cannot be considered in implementing a risk reduction program, nor addressed by emergency response plans.

The responsibility for initiating and assuring completion of a hazard identification activity should be explicitly assigned; frequently it will rest with the facility manager.

Before beginning hazard identification, a key planning step is to determine what types of consequences are of concern. Examples might be:

- Fatalities or injuries to employees and/or the public,
- Release of hazardous material (regardless of the physical damage caused),
- Business interruption,
- Environmental damage, and
- Property damage.

These consequences of concern define the scope of hazard identification activities, and help to define time and staff requirements by determining the level of detail needed. The types of consequences of concern may be dictated by corporate standards, community concerns, individual facility needs (such as determining appropriate spacing to minimize equipment damage), or regulatory requirements.

Many companies are now organizing or enlarging their own in-house capability in the area of hazard identification. For companies with many processes that need review, screening techniques (such as questionnaires and indices) can be used to establish scheduling priorities. When priorities are established, staffing requirements can be determined and resources allocated, and the need for appropriate training can be identified and, if necessary, developed.

Implementation of hazard identification may involve using any of a number of available techniques, or a set of in-house procedures drawing from these techniques. Some of the more common approaches include:

- Checklists--comparisons against codes, standards, and typical hazards previously identified for well-understood operations;
- "What if"--an approach in which a multidisciplinary team generates and addresses a series of "what if"-type questions;
- Hazard and operability study--a structured, systematic review conducted to identify all deviations from the design intent that could potentially yield hazards and/or operability problems; and
- Failure mode and effect analysis--a systematic review of the implications of specific component failures.

These approaches and several others are described further in an AIChE/CCPS document, Guidelines for Hazard Evaluation Procedures, and a number of other documents (see References 33,40,45,57,59,60). The management system should guide the appropriate choice of which techniques will be used, and when each will be used. A good hazard identification approach will detect significant hazards, yield accurate descriptions of hazards in a form adequate for subsequent qualitative or quantitative evaluations, and allow a judgment of the seriousness of each hazard to be made within a reasonable amount of time.

In organizing a hazard identification program, it is useful to include personnel with extensive knowledge of the operation. Thorough hazard identification requires knowledge of the process or operations of concern, operating and maintenance procedures, layout, shutdown capabilities and procedures, interfaces with utilities, and such. In addition, knowledge of hazard evaluation techniques is needed. The number of people required will vary, depending on the techniques employed, but people from diverse backgrounds should participate in order to maximize the creativity of each person. The hazard identification team should draw on the specialized knowledge of others as needed.

Use of written guidelines on hazard identification can help control the consistency and quality of the effort. Figure 6-1 presents a sample table of contents from one plant's process hazards review guidelines handbook. In this plant, the overall guidelines cover identification, evaluation, and control of hazards. The identification process is conducted using a number of different checklists; many contain questions designed to make the user think about various types of hazards.

Hazard identification is an activity that should be conducted periodically throughout the operating lifetime of the process. The frequency of hazard reviews should be determined by the management system, based on factors such as potential consequences of known residual hazards, the time since the process was last reviewed, and the potential for hazards resulting from corrosion, inadequate maintenance, or physical wear. Also, a control mechanism (e.g., an audit) should be introduced to confirm the completion of each hazard review.

The management system should help assure the quality of the hazard identification activities. A number of factors may be used to contribute to this goal. For example,

TABLE OF CONTENTS

Figure 6–1. *Example of Process Hazards Review Guidelines*

hazard identification teams may be led by specialists in process safety; special training may be required to qualify hazard identification team members, and detailed documentation of the hazard identification process may be required. The latter management control approach involves documenting *all* issues considered -- not only those resulting in findings or recommendations. This more detailed documentation facilitates confirmation that all important issues were reviewed during the hazard identification.

6.3 Risk Analysis of Operations

After performing hazard identification in existing operations, as described in Section 6.2, the next component of a successful process risk management program is evaluation and interpretation of the hazards. This activity usually entails an evaluation of both the potential consequences of a hazard and its likelihood of occurrence. These evaluations may be either qualitative or quantitative. (Many available techniques are described in several of AIChE/CCPS's previous publications.) The goals of such evaluations are to determine the significance of a given hazard, to prioritize the hazard for the most cost-effective application of risk-mitigation measures, to help develop risk reduction measures, and to help identify residual risks requiring management attention.

Risk analyses are site-specific and should consider and reflect local meteorological conditions and surrounding populations. If they are qualitative, the output of such studies is usually a prioritized or grouped listing of hazard scenarios. If they are quantitative, they can be used to produce overall measures of risk, such as risk profiles, risk contours, and/or individual risk levels. Figure 6-2 shows examples of the presentation of risk profiles and risk contours.

Management systems designed to support this component must assure that many technical issues are handled consistently and in a manner appropriate to the issue under study. Examples of such issues are listed in Table 6-1.

The management system should offer guidance as to the frequency with which such evaluations should be carried out (e.g., phase in both depth and time). Frequency may be influenced by many factors, such as the inherent hazards of chemicals involved and the proximity of vulnerable populations and facilities. In implementing risk analysis programs, the management system should specify the internal review procedures to employ, and when to use qualitative versus quantitative analysis (e.g., screening evaluations versus detailed cost benefit studies of mitigation).

Control of risk analysis is often achieved through a requirement for management and staff signoffs (technical, management, legal), the establishment of schedules for individual studies, and specification of reporting requirements.

The management system should indicate where the responsibility for risk analysis lies. The responsibility for carrying out such studies may initially be at the corporate level as a few trial or "benchmark" studies are done. In some cases, these studies are introduced through the engineering department. Ultimately, however, the responsibility is usually at the facility level.

If an organization is using detailed quantitative analyses, then ongoing support from trained specialists (e.g., corporate staff or external consultants) will be required.

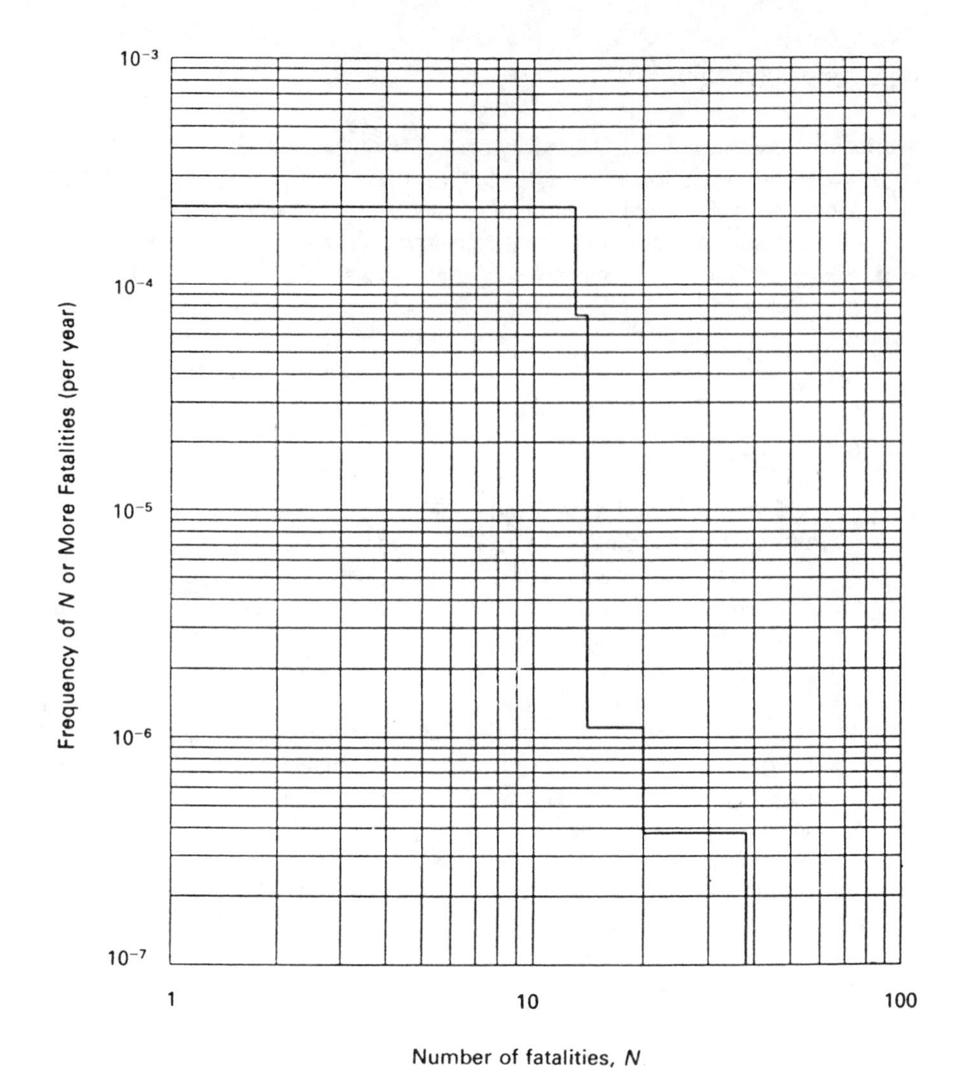

Figure 6.2. *Example Risk Profile. Fatility vs. Frequency Diagram. (This profile presents societal risk from exposure to chlorine release from an unloading system. From* Guidelines for Chemical Process Quantitative Risk Analysis. *New York: AIChE/CCPS, 1989.)*

Table 6-1
Example of Issues to be Considered in Risk Analysis

Procedures for determining the absolute or relative risk levels;
Appropriate sources of (failure) data to support these procedures;
Approved models or algorithms for determining the potential sizes of toxic or flammable vapor clouds, fires, and overpressure zones from explosions;
The criteria--e.g., the toxic concentration of concern--against which the consequences will be determined;
The weather conditions or types of conditions for which the consequence models will be executed;
The ultimate risk measure or format of presentation that will be used;
Determination of whether average populations or separate day/night populations should be used;
The boundaries of specific studies (i.e., one unit vs. entire facility);
"Domino" effects (i.e., effects caused as a result of the initial event).

6.4 Reduction of Risk

Once process risks in ongoing operations have been both identified and evaluated, the acceptability of the risks and the need for risk reduction must be considered. Some examples of potential risk-reducing measures include increasing operator training, substituting less hazardous materials, reducing inventories, modifying equipment (e.g., to handle temperature or pressure excursions or runaway reactions), upgrading protective systems (such as deluge systems), installing additional or improved process control, increasing separation distances, improving monitoring and testing, and changing materials of construction. These various measures would reduce process risk either by reducing the likelihood of occurrence, reducing the consequences of a release, or eliminating some risks altogether.

Planning a risk reduction program requires establishment of philosophies or criteria for evaluating the acceptability of process risks (see examples in Table 6-2). Some major U.S. and European chemical companies (as well as numerous government agencies) are evolving such criteria (see References 2,3). There are two basic approaches to evaluating the acceptability of risks. The more traditional approach is policy-driven and qualitative in nature, and it typically involves implementing risk-mitigation measures wherever these measures are judged appropriate to the hazard. The second approach is quantitative and involves the development of numerical criteria for measuring risk acceptability.

Table 6-2
Examples of Risk Acceptability Criteria

Qualitative

Company X will not knowingly pose a greater risk to the public than it does to its own employees.
Company X will not expose its employees or neighbors to risks that are considered unacceptable, based on industry practice and available technology.
Company X will comply with all applicable regulations and industry guidelines related to acute risks, and will adopt its own standards where regulations do not exist or are inadequate.
Company X will neither undertake nor continue any operations whose associated risks it does not understand or cannot control at a safe level.

Quantitative

The average individual fatal risk level for the public should be less than ______.
The maximum individual fatal risk for employees should be less than ______.
The probability of one or more public fatalities should be less than ______.
The probability of 100 or more public fatalities should be less than ______.

The process safety management system should specify risk-acceptability criteria. These criteria need not necessarily be quantitative or highly specific, but they should help assure consistent decision-making. When dealing with goals for risk levels, it is possible to establish distinct targets or standards for new operations versus existing operations. Even if the goals are the same, there may be different implementation schedules.

Risk reduction program organization requires having clearly defined responsibility for reviewing risk analyses and then deciding upon the action to be taken. The management system should clearly differentiate between responsibility for analyses implementation decisions, assigning each to appropriate personnel.

Upon receipt of a risk analysis for an ongoing operation, there are several courses of action open for implementing risk reduction. These generally include:

- Requesting additional information and the development or evaluation of alternatives,
- Pursuing more detailed evaluations,
- Implementing risk-mitigation measures,
- Accepting and managing the residual risk, and/or
- Ceasing operations (where risk cannot be acceptably managed).

Table 6-3 presents one company's action guidelines.

From a management perspective, it is not sufficient to identify potential process risk- reduction measures. Effective implementation of risk-reduction measures is imperative. This may require quality assurance, supervision, support for ongoing efforts (such as periodic training), and the continuous updating of drawings and procedures. A commitment of resources to the overall program is required for the implementation of the appropriate measures.

Communication channels should be established to allow engineering, maintenance, and operations staff to give their input on perceived hazards and recommended risk reduction on an ongoing basis. These comments can be reviewed at a suitable level, and subsequent recommendations examined at plant level. Procedures that recognize the value of operator intervention into a potentially unsafe situation should also be implemented. Management should create an environment in which operators will not hesitate to provide input on process safety.

In addition to risk-reduction actions that are taken in response to specific risk and hazard studies, many companies also have specific design standards intended to control risks. This subject is discussed in some detail in Chapter 12.

Controlling the risk-reduction process is very important. Once a process risk has been identified and evaluated, it is important to maintain detailed records of subsequent decisions and actions, regardless of the course of action that is followed. This documentation serves as an internal control reference against which implementation actions can be checked to confirm completion. In addition, documentation serves as an historical record of the evolution and development of the activity (see Chapter 4). The documentation also demonstrates prudent and responsible behavior by the firm. An audit program (see Chapter 13) also helps control the risk-reduction process.

Table 6-3
Semiquantitative Ranking of Risks

Class I

Risks (related either to specific processes or general management systems) significant enough to require immediate shutdown of an operating unit until the hazard is mitigated. A unit may not be operated while risk-mitigation measures are being implemented. Stop-gap measures may be used only if a detailed analysis shows that such measures can effectively mitigate the hazards; such measures may be used only on an interim basis (following established variance procedures). In addition, there shall be an immediate initiation of a program to provide a permanent solution.

Example: Bypassing an emergency shutdown system

Class II

Other serious process risks or deficiencies in risk management systems require immediate action to mitigate the potential hazard. If temporary stop-gap measures are used to mitigate the risk, a program to provide a permanent solution should be initiated immediately.

Example: No test program to verify operability of remotely operated block valves.

Class III

Process risks or deficiencies in risk management systems of a less serious nature than those in Class II, and that have less immediacy than those in Class II. These situations should be corrected as soon as reasonably possible to bring the facility's program up to good industry practice.

Example: Process flowsheets need updating.

Class IV

Other areas of possible risk reduction or improvement in risk management systems (advisory in nature).

Example: Failure to follow up accident/incident reports.

6.5 Residual Risk Management

Previous sections of this chapter addressed systems for identifying, analyzing, and reducing to appropriate levels the risks from process operations. With such systems in place, risks can be reduced; however, risks can never be completely eliminated. The purpose of this component of risk management is to manage the risks that remain after implementation of risk controls (i.e., the residual risks).

Process risk management involves analyzing risks, determining their acceptability, and implementing risk-mitigation measures where appropriate. However, risk analysis (whether qualitative or quantitative) is based upon a series of assumptions and uncertainties. For example, risk analysis is likely to assume a given plant layout and design as well as certain operating procedures and certain neighboring facilities (and distances from vulnerable locations). The analysis may be based on current understanding of chemical hazards (e.g., toxicity, reactivity) and hazard modeling methodologies, both of which are evolving.

Managing residual risks should involve ongoing review and reconsideration of the underlying assumptions and uncertainties. Changes in these assumptions and uncertainties may change the acceptability of the risks.

Management systems should assure thorough documentation of the uncertainties and assumptions, and assign responsibility for both maintaining on-going awareness of changes and for periodically initiating an active search for new information in relevant technical fields (see Chapter 14). In addition, the process safety audit program (see Chapter 13) should periodically confirm the assumptions made in the risk analysis.

Residual risk management should also include periodic review of the identified risks to assure that they have not grown to unacceptable levels. Through the introduction of new "neighboring" units, or the development of property adjacent to the plant site, or other factors external to a specific unit, the level of risk presented by the unit may increase. The management system should prompt periodic risk analysis to confirm that residual risks are not surpassing corporate guidelines for acceptability.

Assumptions made in the scoping of earlier risk analysis should also be reviewed periodically. For example, there may be incident scenarios that were not analyzed in earlier studies since facility design or other factors compromised their credibility. Subsequent changes may require reconsideration of such exclusions. Alternatively, a subsequent review may identify scenarios not considered previously, either because the scenarios went unidentified, or because subsequent incidents raised new issues.

The assumptions made regarding failure frequencies should also be examined during periodic reviews. As operating history is gained, it may be necessary to modify the assumptions used in earlier risk analyses. Review of maintenance history may also suggest areas needing further study.

Formal documentation of periodic reviews and communication of the results of risk analysis are also critical (see Chapter 4). A technique used by some companies is to require the formal recertification of process risk reviews on a regularly scheduled basis. Periodic auditing of the results by an established internal review group is important to assure that hazard identification and risk review procedures are being properly and consistently applied across the entire organization (see Chapter 12).

Results of all such studies should be circulated in a timely manner through an established communication channel that includes all key reviewers, decision-makers, and authorizations. Follow-up examination of action items is essential for effective management control.

6.6 Process Management during Emergencies

An important component of process risk management is the management and control of processes during emergencies. The purpose is to control all relevant processes (those that experienced the incident, could worsen the incident, or could have an impact because of the incident) such that consequences are minimized. There are two parts to this component: (1) management of the particular process that had experienced the emergency incident, and (2) management of other processes that interact with, or are near to, that particular process. (This component does not address emergency response team planning or organization, although these are major factors that must be considered in managing the emergency. The critical component of community integration in emergency planning has also been excluded from this discussion.)

Organizing for emergency response must occur long before an emergency situation arises. Emergency response planning should indicate who will be responsible for process management during emergencies. Process control rooms should be designed to offer protection from process hazards, or remote process control locations should be provided. Emergency plans should be practiced through periodic drills.

In some situations, a response team may have to take corrective action, such as manually shutting valves. Members of the team (on all shifts), including the team leader and emergency coordinator, should be knowledgeable of the various processes in the facility. In large facilities, this responsibility can be spread among several individuals who must be kept informed of significant process changes through management-of-change procedures (see Chapter 7). Such information should also be made a part of the periodic refresher training.

Implementation of emergency process management programs requires more than just staff preparedness. Early detection and assessment of an impending emergency can contribute to successful control and mitigation. Process control systems should be designed to provide rapid feedback of key information on the cause of each emergency, and operators should be knowledgeable and trained in emergency response procedures. Such procedures should be fully documented and readily available for reference. Appropriate shutdown switches or kill buttons should be provided, but it is also important that staff know when other courses of action (e.g., transfer of material to a different vessel) may be more suitable. In computer-controlled processes, emergency shutdown sequences should be programmed-in; however, operators should also know how to respond in case of computer failure.

During an emergency, other processes on the plant site must be managed to minimize the implications of the emergency. These processes should neither worsen nor escalate the emergency, nor should they be adversely affected by the incident. Information on processes to be shut down during emergencies (e.g. those nearby the emergency, or those providing feedstreams or taking product) should be included in the emergency procedure, along with information on those processes that should not be shut down. Appropriate isolation requirements should also be identified.

Lines of communication should be established, and the appropriate contact persons and information to be transferred should be identified to respond to situations that require decisions during emergency response. Attention should be given to inventories of hazardous materials that might need to be transferred to another vessel or location during an emergency.

Facility audits can be used as a management control to validate the existence and adequacy of procedures, shutdown lists, notification lists, and other key instructions and documents. Such audits should occur regularly to assure that emergency response programs are kept current. Audit interviews can assess operator knowledge and adequacy of training.

6.7 Encouraging Client and Supplier Companies to Adopt Similar Risk Management Practices

The components of risk management discussed thus far deal mainly with the management of risk at one's own facility or plant. However, a comprehensive program also addresses systems that can be put into place to encourage customers, supplier companies, and hazardous waste disposal companies to practice similar levels of risk management. Included among the target organizations for this effort are the transportation companies that carry feed materials from suppliers, product materials to customers and contract manufacturers, and hazardous wastes to disposal firms. The overall purpose of this component is to create a level of risk management that is suitable and consistent among all industry players. The underlying philosophy for all companies to understand is that serious incidents affect the viability of the entire industry--not just their own company. Everyone handling, using, storing, or processing hazardous materials will suffer if a serious incident occurs because of poor risk management by one company. It is important, therefore, to encourage and persuade others to adopt similar high standards of risk management.

These programs require commitment from management and an organized coordinated effort among many functions in a firm (e.g., sales, legal, purchasing, distribution, safety, etc.). Because these programs can directly affect intercompany relationships, they cannot be undertaken without strong senior management support.

Various strategies can be used to encourage good risk management in other firms. Strict contractual arrangements, memoranda of understanding, inspections, and cooperative agreements can all be satisfactory, depending upon one company's knowledge of the other company's operations. When implementing a program of this kind, marketing and sales personnel and buyers should be aware of such strategies so that communication with customers and suppliers can occur early in the process. Business managers should also be involved in the process to demonstrate the overall commitment to this philosophy.

Contractual arrangements can be made very strong, while cooperative agreements are the least binding form of encouragement. The latter can be effective with long-time, well-known customers and suppliers; the former could be used with those who are new or unknown. Memoranda of understanding can also be used in a less formal, more cooperative arrangement.

Inspections of supplier and customer facilities and procedures are currently being conducted by many companies, particularly the industry leaders, and should be prepared, regardless of the formality or informality of any risk management arrangement.

It is also important to encourage and seek cooperation from carrier companies. Many of the large chemical companies periodically conduct detailed surveys to review trucking companies, and include rail carriers in their transportation risk management activities. Large pipeline and marine transport companies have also become active practitioners of such policies.

6.8 Selection of Businesses with Acceptable Risk

When process risks have been analyzed, there will be some situations where the risk is too great to be acceptable. In some such cases, the feasible risk-mitigation measures will not be sufficient to make the risk acceptable. It may be necessary to leave a business when this situtation occurs.

Another area that needs proper process safety management consideration is that of acquisitions. Although the tight timing involved and the desire to minimize the number of people with knowledge of the pending acquisition can cause complications, process safety is becoming increasingly recognized as an area that needs pre-acquisition review.

The current position of many companies is to obtain information on significant process risks and potential liabilities, sometimes using outside consultants who may be more acceptable to the target facility. So long as the checklist used to identify risks or liabilities of concern is periodically updated to reflect new regulatory hurdles and the findings of past reviews, this may suffice as a first-level screening process.

A longer-term process risk management view would suggest the need for a more comprehensive initial review. Such a review would include gathering data on typical hazards/risks associated with a certain type of design or process, as well as information on other potential problems or difficulties that may be encountered from an operability, regulatory, insurability, or community relations point of view. Middle management, as represented by plant managers and their group or division managers, are most capable of supplying information quickly on such issues. Specific technical recommendations or advice may also be appropriate if a new chemical or process (or a chemical or process new to the company) is involved. Such technical expertise may be located in the engineering or research and development functions.

Only by considering such information on hazards and risks up front can a company determine whether the new business will be compatible with the existing risk guidelines. Any operation that falls outside the guidelines should have estimates of the time and dollars necessary to bring it into internal compliance included in the financial considerations, so that a more accurate total acquisition cost can be determined. This review process also allows the firm to recognize that there may be a transition period during which management of a higher level of risk may be required.

7
Management of Change

7.1 Overview

Changes to facilities that produce, use, handle, and store hazardous materials are necessary for many reasons. In properly managing such change, an essential first step is to define what is meant by change. Change to process and equipment technology, as defined in Chapter 4, is straightforward. The definition of "change," however, needs to be broadened to include *all* modifications to equipment and procedures, including additions and deletions, but excluding "replacement in kind." Change also includes modifications to an organization that may affect process safety. The next essential step is to train all personnel in managing process safety to:

1) "understand" what is meant by change,
2) recognize and identify such changes as they occur, and
3) flag such changes for appropriate review.

It is widely recognized that new facilities or major plant modifications need to be thoroughly reviewed to ensure safe operation, and this need is typically addressed through capital project reviews (see Chapter 5). However, even small changes can have catastrophic consequences if done improperly. When taken in this context, changes can range from installation of a new piece of process equipment, to installation of a different gasket material, to a simple instrument setpoint adjustment outside of normal limits -- a procedural modification.

All such changes must be identified and reviewed *before* implementation. At the same time, the process operator must have the flexibility to maintain continuity of operation within established safe operating limits. These safe operating limits need to be made a part of the operating manual and/or procedures, as discussed in Chapter 4 of these Guidelines. The operator should be allowed to make necessary changes to process conditions that do not exceed the safe operating limits. Operation outside of these limits, however, requires formal review and approval by a pre-determined procedure. In determining approval level, cost alone should not be used as the criterion.

Organizational changes can also have safety implications, particularly when personnel with specific knowledge and expertise are transferred or retire. Prior to such moves, replacement staff must be trained to adequately perform important safety functions. Another important consideration is the overall level of staffing. If key personnel leave with no replacements to take over, not only is a wealth of knowledge lost, but extra work is placed upon the staff who remain. This may result in higher levels of stress, increased likelihood of human error, and the taking of unsafe shortcuts by operating personnel.

Management of change is a critical element in a process safety management program. This element includes the following components:

- Change of process technology,
- Change of facility,
- Organizational changes that may have an impact on process safety,
- Variance procedures,
- Permanent changes,
- Temporary changes.

Each of these components is discussed in this chapter.

7.2 Change of Process Technology

Six major reasons for needing to make process changes are listed below:

- Maintain process continuity,
- Compensation for equipment unavailability,
- Startup or end-of-run shutdown,
- Experimentation (e.g., yield or quality improvement, new product),
- Change in production rate,
- New equipment.

A management system for process changes should incorporate planning for each of these situations, and should consider the unique circumstances of each.

During normal operation, it is the prime responsibility of the operating personnel to maintain smooth operation. In traditional plants, it is not unusual for a process operator to make numerous changes per shift to maintain optimum operating conditions. Some process parameters may be varied over a wide range and still remain within safe operating limits, while others may require tight control. Establishing safe operating limits is a means of controlling the process operator's activities, and should be implemented by incorporating them in the operating manual or procedures (see Chapter 4). In computer-controlled plants, much of this activity is performed by the computer system. However, operators still must monitor operations and respond to alarms.

In emergency situations, where there is no time for review and approval, the established procedure should be to shut down rather than operate outside of established safe operating limits.

Deviation from safe operating limits, under normal conditions, is sometimes the result of nothing more than unnecessarily tight boundaries on an operating variable

However, organizational responsibility for making this judgment should not be placed upon the operator alone. There should be clear procedures and instructions implemented that indicate that running an operation outside of established safe operating limits is not permitted until the proposed changes have been formally reviewed and authorized by appropriate management personnel.

When an unexpected deviation or human error under normal operations requires a change in process conditions to values outside of established operating limits, actions should be taken to return the system to safe conditions. The operating procedures should incorporate contingency provisions, but all contingencies cannot be foreseen. When such events occur, they should be captured and recorded in the process history so lessons can be learned and observed.

During the planning and design of a new process, considerable thought goes into defining proper operating conditions to avoid certain safety or operability problems. Sometimes these problems cannot be recognized by operating personnel without prior indoctrination, and appropriate alarms and shutdowns are installed. It is especially important to control changes to alarm and interlock setpoints, including bypassing, and changes to process control logic by requiring review of such changes. Further, as more processes are designed to operate on computer control, software changes to the program that controls the process must be adequately reviewed prior to the change. Reviews to changes in alarm levels, interlock setpoints, process control software, and other critical monitors and controls should involve staff who have the appropriate knowledge and experience to identify the process safety implications of the change.

Occasionally process conditions must be changed to compensate for unavailable equipment. For example, failure of a pump might require increasing pressure in the vessel to allow pressure transfer to the next vessel. Thorough review and approval should be required before implementation if operation outside of normal safe operating limits is contemplated. In this example, the vessels, piping, and transfer hoses involved must be able to safely withstand the increased pressure. When pressurizing a tank, the adequacy of the tank vent and many other factors also need to be confirmed. Another example occurs when a back-up safety system (e.g., a flare) is taken out of service. Although this change would not affect normal operation, the ability to respond to process upsets may be compromised, and should prompt a review process. Therefore a good process change review is required whenever a process is to continue operation in the absence of any normal equipment, and the review should specifically require consideration of the potential need for special hazard control measures. Accountability for assuring that such reviews are performed should be assigned to staff likely to know when equipment goes out of service (e.g., a shift supervisor). However, the review procedure should require involvement of staff who can assess the process safety impact and, if necessary, suggest controls.

A particularly busy and potentially hazardous time for any process is initial start-up. It is during this time that many problems that require changes to process conditions or equipment are encountered. Such changes must be methodically and comprehensively reviewed to ensure that safety is not compromised. However, in the urgency of the moment, there may be temptation to compromise safety, either knowingly or inadvertently. Therefore, good process change procedures need to be in place before startup so that proposed changes can be controlled (reviewed and approved) in a timely manner.

A good variance procedure is also important as many unique situations are encountered during initial plant startup. Since many problems are encountered on the night shifts and weekends, it is important to organize personnel assignments so that these shifts include staff with the knowledge, judgment, and authority to approve process changes, or have specific call-in procedures.

Often during initial and subsequent startups, certain alarms and interlocks may have to be bypassed. It may not be practical to issue process changes each time the unit is started up. For those situations where operation outside of normal safe operating limits is required, appropriate procedures should be included in the operating manual or procedures to address the organizational, control, and implementation aspects of these bypasses. The procedures should specify who has the authority to operate bypasses and under what conditions these bypasses can remain activated. They should also address who will specify and who will implement measures to minimize the results of an upset condition. Also, adequate warning should be provided to operators so that they are alerted that the normal systems are inoperable. Similarly, specific procedures should be in place to address how safety devices are to be bypassed and/or tested. At the conclusion of the startup, there should be confirmation that all alarms and interlocks have been returned to normal operation.

One of the most common situations that requires a change in process conditions is testing to improve yield or quality, or simply to produce a new product or product grade. Most tests are conducted first in laboratory or pilot-scale equipment and receive some safety/hazard review for these runs. However, a separate review should be performed while planning such tests for full-scale process equipment (i.e., before the test is run). Any change requiring use of new raw materials, additives, or catalysts (or elimination of a normally used material) should be considered a process change. Particular areas of concern when using new materials are effects on corrosion rate, vapor generation, solids formation, flammability, toxicity, reactivity, byproduct formation, stability, and the like. In many situations, improvements in yield or quality require operation within a different parameter range, and could result in increased risk. There should be clear organizational responsibility for reviewing proposed experimental changes and specifying hazard control measures to be taken. The expected effects of tests should be clearly communicated to operators, so they can help identify deviations from anticipated process behavior.

7.3 Change of Facility

When an equipment change (other than a simple replacement in kind) is being contemplated, there should be careful consideration of the process safety implications. The organizational responsibility for approving such changes should be clearly defined, and approval only should occur after an appropriate review has been completed. The implementation of the change should be limited to the specific equipment changes that have been reviewed and approved. There should be control over the equipment change process, achieved through mechanisms such as requiring documentation of all work performed, and having both operating and maintenance personnel sign off on the agreement of the work done with the approved work orders.

Many equipment changes will require a corresponding change in process conditions. Major new equipment should be included in capital appropriation requests and be reviewed as part of any new capital project (see Chapter 5). There are, however, certain types of equipment changes made in the field that are not included in a capital project review. Some examples are:

- Process improvements,
- Piping rearrangements,
- Experimental equipment,
- Temporary equipment,
- Decommissioning,
- Change in materials of construction,
- Change in computer programs,
- Change in instrumentation.

Although many changes may appear harmless, without proper review process hazards can be created. For example, cross-connections could be made that, under certain conditions, could cause a backflow of materials into systems not designed to handle them.

Equipment changes not covered by capital project reviews must still be controlled by a review and approval procedure. There should be systems for assuring that these changes are identified in advance so that a review will be scheduled. Appropriate personnel should be involved in the review. A checklist of issues to be considered helps assure appropriate review. Completion of the review should be documented to assure accountability and facilitate subsequent audit.

Figure 7-1 is an example of an equipment change request form. This firm's procedure specifies who should approve the change, indicates issues to be considered, and requires submission of completed review forms to a central individual who can review and verify the proper use of the procedures.

7.4 Organizational Changes

Within an operating firm, personnel changes may be more frequent than hardware or process changes. Arrivals and departures will occur at both the operating and management levels.

Personnel changes present challenges for the process safety management. New staff must learn both process characteristics and their roles in the process safety management systems. Both documentation (see Chapter 4) and training (see Chapter 10) are key elements in this transaction.

Similarly, changes in organizational responsibilities (even where no change of specific people is involved) may require careful review of process safety management systems to assure that all process safety responsibilities are appropriately assigned (see Chapter 3).

The departure of experienced staff creates special challenges. Every facility seems to have a certain individual who has worked at the site since startup and has been involved with all major expansions. This individual knows where all the underground piping runs, why equipment is operated in a certain manner, what major accidents have occurred, and many other valuable pieces of information that may never have been documented. Even if a site has implemented review and documentation programs for new projects, the documentation for changes made to older facilities may not be

Initiation: (to be completed by originator)

Originator:____________________________Date:_______________
Description of Project: (attach sketch, P&ID, etc.)

____
____
____

Process fluid:_______________ Operating press:_______________ Temp:_______________

Approval: (to be submitted by field supervisor)
Ticket No.:_______________

1. Operations assistant______________________________ Date________________________
2. Maintenance assistant______________________________ Date________________________
3. Technical team leader______________________________ Date________________________

cc: TSTL for files TSO assigned_______________

Process Review: (to be completed by TSO) TSO_______________ Date_______________

( ) Construction package completed
( ) Process impacts
( ) Scope defined (attach marked-up or revised P&IDs)
( ) Product quality impacts
( ) P&ID review (interdisciplinary)

Mechanical Review: (to be completed by PST/MEG/I/E as needed)
PST_______________ MEG_______________ I/E_______________ Date_______________

( ) MEG requirements
( ) Painting/insulation ___________
( ) Materials of construction
( ) Relief protection review
( ) I/E requirements
( ) Special inspection required
( ) Pipe spec: ___________ ( ) MAWP
( ) Gasket material: ___________
( ) Testing requirements:
( ) Hydrostatic test pressure: ___________ (hold at least 10 min)
( ) In-service test
( ) Visual
( ) Radiography

Construction: (to be completed by field supervisor and inspector)

( ) Construction drawings prepared
( ) Equipment folder updated
( ) P&IDs updated
( ) On-lines updated
( ) Car seal list updated
( ) Loop diagrams/folders updated
( ) RV list updated
( ) Fugitive emissions list updated
( ) Spare parts stocked
( ) Painting/insulation
( ) Steam tracing installed/list updated
( ) Appropriate bleeds/vents/drains
( ) Blind list updated
( ) SOME review
( ) Operating procedures
( ) HAZCOM updated
( ) Construction/testing complete and per design

Field supervisor__________________________________ Date________________________
Inspector__________________________________ Date________________________

Forward completed form to technical support team leader.

Figure 7–1. *Equipment Change Request Form*

available except in the minds of select individuals. When these individuals leave, this part of the "company memory" is lost.

When organizational changes cause these "historians" to leave (whether they retire, are transferred, or move to other firms), it is important to have them document as much of the facility's technical history as possible before they leave. In particular, any unique operating knowledge or characteristics should be documented. The rationale behind design decisions and operating practices should also be captured. A similar case can be made for individuals transferred to other assignments within a facility.

The loss of multiple personnel can be even more significant. As companies continue to streamline staffing, there comes a point beyond which any further reductions can have serious safety implications. This may not be apparent under normal operation, but in an emergency, if staffing levels and/or staff experience levels are too low, a minor problem could easily escalate to become a major incident. Staff organization should be tested for consistency with the operational demands of all different circumstances, including both normal operations and emergencies. Special care should be taken to assure that staffing plans are not inadvertently based on overlapping staff assignments (e.g., where a key operator is responsible for the safe shutdown of equipment and is also responsible for the emergency response team).

The above concerns can be managed by planning (and adopting a policy for) a minimum staffing and experience level for each process unit. Any change in staff would require a review to ensure that these minimum levels are not violated. When staffing experience in a unit becomes too low, certain measures should be initiated, such as increased training, the temporary retention of transferees, or the engaging of retirees as temporary consultants.

7.5 Variance Procedures

In any operation, situations arise that were not foreseen when the operating procedures were developed. At such times, personnel may want to conduct operations in a way that differs from, or contradicts, the process technology or the standard operating procedures.

To assure that these deviations from normal practice do not create unacceptable risks, it is important to have a variance procedure, or to have incorporated the same means of control into other management systems. The variance procedure will require review of the planned deviation, and acceptance of the risks it poses. The variance procedure should require explanation of the deviation planned; the reasons it is necessary; the safety, health, and environmental considerations; control measures to be taken; and the duration of the variance. Variances should require approval by a suitable level of management, based on the process risks involved. Also, they should be documented to assure consistent understanding by all affected individuals and departments of what specific departure from normal practice is to be allowed.

7.6 Permanent Changes

Having defined the types of changes that would require a process safety review, an initiating mechanism must be provided to allow changes to be documented and the review process to be completed. Most organizations that have process change procedures specify requirements for documenting the change. Table 7-1 lists the contents of one company's form for managing technology change. The Company's test authorization form is shown in Figure 7-2. Notice that the items covered in Table 7-1 address planning, organizing, implementing, and controlling the change process (see Figure 7-3)

The process change form may be used in conjunction with other plant programs, such as the maintenance work order system, the purchase order system, or the capital project review system. When maintenance involves a process change, there may be an appropriate section on the work order form to indicate the need for a process change review. The required type of review may vary, depending on the change proposed. The simplest form of review is a checklist where various safety considerations are listed and available for review by the authorized individual. This form of review may be appropriate for simple changes where the impact of the change is well understood. If, however, there is some doubt about the implications of a certain change, or if a considerable design effort is involved, the person initiating the change order, or the person who approves the change order, should have the option to require a higher level

Table 7-1
Example of Process Change Form Contents

- Description and purpose of the change
  - Specifically, what change(s) is being proposed?
  - What are the test details? What technology and facilities are being changed?
  - Why is the change being proposed? Is it necessary?
- Duration of the change
- Technical basis for the change:
  - What is the technical basis for the change? (If the approvers and authorizer do not understand the technical basis for the change, how can they assess the hazards of scale-up?)
- Safety, Health and Environmental considerations
  - What are they?
  - Is a formal process hazards review required?
  - Does the change significantly affect any previously conducted risk analysis?
- Process Documentation:
  - Are changes required?
  - Operating procedures?
  - Mechanical procedures?
  - Piping and instrument diagrams?
  - Others?
- Personnel Training
  - What training and communication regarding the change will be required?
- Pre-startup inspection required?
- Level of approval and authorization

Test Authorization No. TA–C–____________________ Date: __________
Product Name: ____________________ Product Code: __________
Area: ____________________ Pounds Proposed: __________
Title: ____________________ Building No.: __________
Prepared by: ____________________ Financial Risk: __________
Responsible for test and test conclusion: ____________________

Purpose of test:

Duration of test:

Standard involved:

CAS No.: __________

TSCA inventory:
( ) No change ( ) New chemical ( ) Included on TSCA inventory ( ) Exemption or explanation attached*
Analytical control or specifications: ( ) No change ( ) Change described under test details
Process hazards review: ( ) Required before test—see attached ( ) Not required
Material safety data sheet: ( ) Revision required ( ) No change ( ) New raws (see attached)
Packaging and shipping classifications: ( ) Revision required ( ) No change
Waste minimization discussed: ( ) Attached ( ) Not applicable
Air permit or revision needed: ( ) Yes ( ) No
TCPA EHS: ( ) Yes ( ) No (refer to PHM guidelines, Section IX)
Technical basis for change:

Test details (include Safety and Occupational Health and Waste Disposal):

Have operating instructions been prepared and approved?
( ) Yes—see attached ( ) Not required

Distribution:

Approved by: Business Division

Area Env. Ctrl. Coord. Date	Research Supervisor Date	Business Manager** Date
R&D TSCA Coord.* Date	CWCL Lab Supv./Anal.Res.Supv.** Date	Product Manager** Date
Tech. Service Mgr.** Date	Mechanical Supv.** Date	
	PHM Coordinator*** Date	

Authorized by:

Area Manager Date	Business Unit Manager** Date	Plant Manager** Date

* Required if new chemicals are used, made, or isolated which are not included on the TSCA inventory.
** Mark not required where applicable.
*** Required if EHS is involved, per PHM guidelines, Section IX.

Figure 7–2. *Test Authorization Form for Technology/Field Changes*

Change Authorization Form Contents	Management System Function: Planning	Organizing	Implementing	Controlling
Description		●		
Duration		●		
Reference Documentation (e.g., work order)		●		
Process safety impact			●	
Process documentation changes needed			●	
Type of review required	●			
Deficiencies noted			●	
Required approvals	●			
Verification				●

Figure 7–3. *Change Authorization Coverage of Management System Functions*

of review during the planning process. Typically these higher levels of review could include:

- design (what if?) review, and/or
- hazard and operability (HAZOP) study, and/or
- failure modes and effects analysis (FMEA).

In the same context, there should also be provisions in the organization to request specific individuals to participate in the review, depending on the nature of the change, or to have a committee that reviews the change. Additional reviews might be required by maintenance, instrument, electrical, process control, environmental, safety, engineering or utilities specialists. The review committee concept is particularly good if all departments are adequately represented, as this allows uniform treatment of process changes.

After the change is made, but prior to actual implementation, a pre-startup review should be conducted. This review, which is a control mechanism, would evaluate the installation of any new equipment or instrumentation for any safety implications, and ensure that all procedures had been modified and appropriate training been provided to operating personnel. A pre-startup checklist or other documentation used as part of a capital project review system could be used. Only following the pre-startup review and correction of any deficiencies should final authorization to implement the change be given.

During the implementation phase, should any additional changes be required, the original change order could be revised and re-authorized, or if the changes required are substantial, a new change order might be required.

Each process change should be fully documented, preferably following a standard format. Upon approval to implement, the completed form should be posted or kept on file in the area. Additional documentation, such as revisions to the operating manual and piping/instrument or electrical drawings, should be made a part of the review process for the process change. These changes may be made by hand on a master copy and then made permanent the next time the manual or drawings are updated. Similarly, for computer-controlled processes, changes to programming must be thoroughly documented and explained.

Copies of process changes should also be kept in the project files to ensure that proper documentation of design changes is maintained. These changes should be acknowledged as part of the ongoing process hazards or risk reviews conducted at regular intervals.

Finally, as with any procedure, a regular audit should be conducted to verify that the procedure is being implemented properly, particularly with respect to review, approval, and documentation.

7.7 Temporary Changes

There should be no differentiation between the things to consider for changes that are intended to be permanent versus those changes that will have a limited life, i.e., be "temporary" in nature. If the right set of conditions occurs, a hazard will proceed to an incident, regardless of whether the changes were permanent or temporary. A temporary change made without proper review caused the Flixborough disaster (a major process plant explosion which killed 28 people). Other examples of how plant modifications have resulted in accidents are included in References 47,67.

In many respects, "temporary" changes require closer scrutiny, since the engineering controls or hardware needed for a permanent solution are not present, and reliance is often placed on adminstrative controls or alernative hardware solutions. Accordingly, additional considerations that are specific to temporary changes are listed below:

- A time limit for temporary changes must be defined, requiring re-approval for any extensions. Too often temporary changes become permanent because either the change is perceived to be beneficial, or no effort is made to remove the temporary system.
  Without proper documentation, these changes will become part of the process, but the safety implications of these changes may not be incorporated into the procedures. A temporary change should be considered permanent, and should be reviewed and documented as such, after a predefined number of extensions.
- An additional control step needs to be added to ensure that all modified equipment and procedures are returned to their normal mode at the end of the approved time for the change, unless the duration of the change was extended.

In summary, for all process changes, whether temporary or permanent, the basic and fundamental elements for managing process change, as listed and described in Table 7-1, must be considered. Those that are appropriate to the temporary change must be addressed along with appropriate documentation.

8
Process and Equipment Integrity

8.1 Overview

Any equipment used to handle or process hazardous materials should be designed, built, installed, and maintained to control the risk of releases and other accidents. Of primary concern are those components that could release hazardous materials as a result of a single failure, or those components whose operation is critical during an equipment or system malfunction. Well-designed equipment cannot ensure process safety if it fails prematurely, or if it does not operate in the event of an emergency. Design procedures have been discussed in Chapter 5. This chapter addresses the management system necessary to help ensure that equipment is constructed according to design, installed properly, and then adequately maintained.

The components of the process and equipment integrity element are:

- Reliability engineering,
- Materials of construction,
- Fabrication and inspection procedures,
- Installation procedures,
- Preventive maintenance,
- Process, hardware, and systems inspection and testing,
- Maintenance procedures,
- Alarm and instrument management,
- Demolition procedures.

Each of these components is discussed in this chapter.

8.2 Reliability Engineering

Reliability engineering is the process of evaluating how long a system and its individual components can be operated safely before they must be taken out of service for maintenance or replacement. Knowing the reliability of a piece of equipment is important in planning its installation and maintenance (see Reference 14). For example, a piece of equipment that will require frequent maintenance should be readily accessible, both to operating personnel who may be responsible for isolating and preparing the equipment for maintenance, and to maintenance personnel and their equipment. High or frequent maintenance requirements might suggest the need for substitution of equipment better suited to the operating conditions. High maintenance equipment may also need to have standby units or bypasses installed to maintain continuity of operations, and call for an adequate stock of spare parts to allow timely repair. The same reasoning applies to equipment that must be taken out of service for inspections or testing as part of a preventive maintenance program.

The process safety management system should identify: (1) the objectives of reliability engineering, and (2) equipment critical to process safety. With these planning decisions, mechanisms can be established to collect data on actual operating and equipment history. Whenever any maintenance is performed on a piece of equipment, important information should be recorded, including the condition of the equipment prior to performing any work, the actual work performed, the results of any tests or inspections conducted, and the personnel who did the work (including contractors). These data should be organized to facilitate ready access by personnel involved in planning future maintenance, or those involved in specifying new equipment. Computers are an excellent tool for storing and organizing equipment maintenance histories.

The personnel involved in reviewing and analyzing data must have suitable training to be able to identify those potential problems or trends that might indicate that future reliability is questionable.

The final step is to have a means of controlling the system to ensure that the required data are collected and analyzed, and that appropriate action has been taken in response to the conclusions of the reliability analysis. A reasonable approach is to conduct a routine audit of equipment files to determine compliance.

8.3 Materials of Construction

Use of improper materials of construction, during both initial installation and subsequent maintenance of operating facilities, can have catastrophic consequences. To assure that appropriate materials are used, a facility should adopt piping and vessel standards that are appropriate to the hazards present. Responsibility for the adoption of vessel and piping standards should be clearly designated. In many cases, available industry standards (e.g., ASME Pressure Vessel Codes) can be adopted; however, the process safety management system should address the organizational issue of who will identify the standards to be followed, who will monitor changes in the industry standards used, and who will communicate these standards and changes within the firm. Vessel and piping specifications should be supplemented by systems to assure that the materials actually installed are the correct ones.

When severity of risks is high, it may also be appropriate to adopt a tracking system-- especially one for tracking materials of construction from the mills until the pipe, vessel, or other component is installed in the facility. Figure 8-1 illustrates a job flowchart for tracking material.

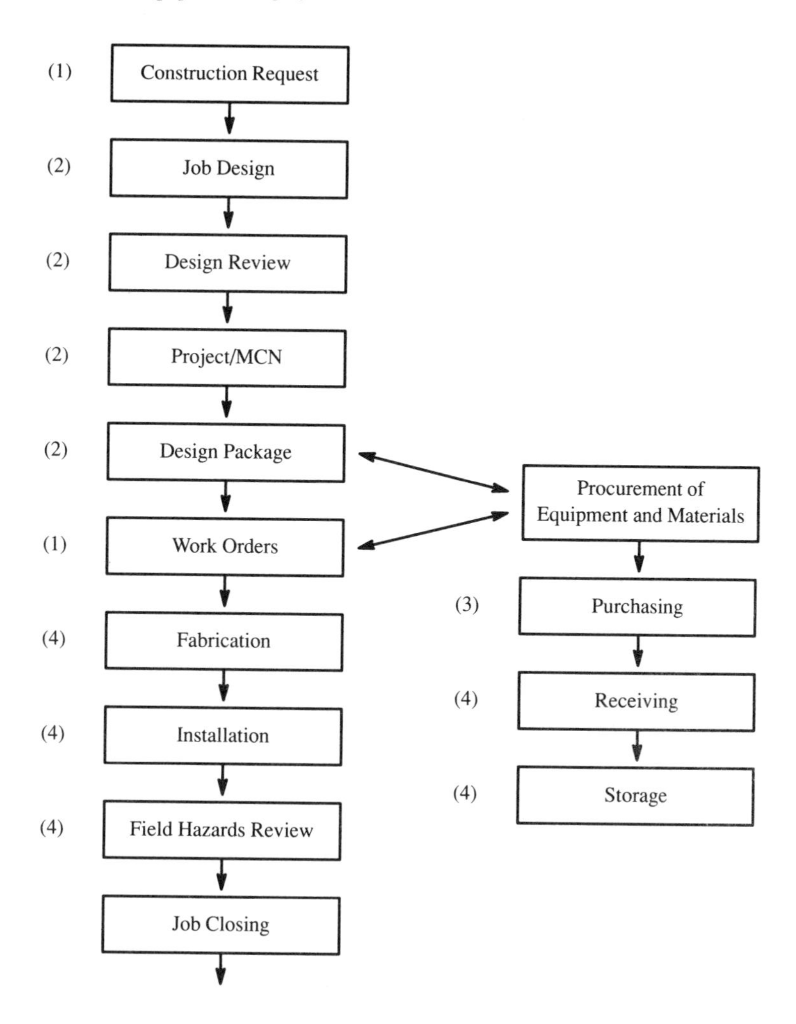

(1) Initiator of work designates PMI in the title and/or description of the job.

(2) Specify proper materials of construction and inspection requirements (verification). Document exceptions approved by area supervisor and metallurgist. The person responsible for each job must give vendors/fabricators, etc., all the appropriate information and specifications required at the start of the job. Special tests/procedures and tests reports, if needed, must be requested and responsibility for each phase must be assigned. Special tests may include chemical composition with mill certifications, tensile and Charpy impact tests, radiographic tests, etc. A materials consultant should be contacted when needed.

(3) Purchase orders designated PMI and state "no substitutes for specified material of construction"; specify proper material of construction; and detail certifications, markings, color coding analytical verifications, special handling at receiving, etc., required.

(4) Documentation checked. Analysis done as defined by area, and documented and tagged.

Figure 8–1. *Job Flowchart for Tracking Material ("Positive Material Identification" or "PMI")*

A material tracking program can serve a control function in the process safety management system. Implementation of an effective material tracking program requires a considerable amount of planning, as well as an evaluation of potential suppliers who are willing to provide the necessary documentation with the finished products. At the plant level, considerable planning needs to be expended in establishing a material tracking program for some higher risk operations, while using more conventional methods for other operations. One effective mechanism is to establish separate accounts for ordering materials under the material tracking program. Thus, when an order is received by a pre-approved supplier, it is clear that special documentation requirements will be followed.

Material tracking starts by requiring verification of materials of construction from the mills by way of unique heat numbers and other data (e.g., Charpy impact test results for low-temperature steels). When pipes, valves, and fittings are manufactured, the heat numbers are supplied with all finished products when delivered to the customer. The receipt and subsequent use of materials are tracked in the facility, with heat numbers again providing an effective tracking mechanism. Color coding is another tracking option, especially for components where specific part-by-part records are not needed.

The use of a material tracking system requires integration of parts tracking information, materials use requirements, and data capture needs with existing engineering, maintenance, and operations management systems. Assurance that the material tracking system is working should include periodic audit of the equipment suppliers' and outside fabricators' facilities.

8.4 Fabrication and Inspection Procedures

Vessel and piping fabrication requirements should be clearly specified in the mechanical design package. During fabrication, a quality assurance program should be in place to ensure that equipment is built according to design and meets all applicable codes and standards.

The process safety management system should include mechanisms to assure that appropriately qualified (and, where appropriate, certified) craftsman are used. Since vessel and piping fabrication are frequently performed by vendors, management controls may have to extend into the vendor's shop.

The management system should also ensure that all vendors' standards and work practices meet requirements. It is useful to have a set of standards for all vendors to follow. This presents organizational issues, both in designating responsibility for standards development and in managing the contractual relationship with vendors to enforce the standards. In addition, some level of auditing is a useful control mechanism.

Documentation of tests and inspections performed during fabrication provides another control mechanism, and also generates important baseline data for comparison with future in-service tests and inspections conducted as part of a preventive maintenance program. For vessels built according to the ASME code, code certificates should be retained. As-built drawings, along with all other documentation, e.g., materials of construction verification, should be placed in an accessible equipment file.

All documentation should be signed and dated by the person responsible for verifying the data.

8.5 Installation Procedures

Codes and standards are generally not specific in addressing the field installation of equipment. Planning on the part of construction management personnel is necessary to develop adequate quality control systems to ensure that equipment is installed according to design specifications and equipment manufacturers' instructions. According to Kletz (see Reference 46), a majority of piping failures are caused by a combination of unsatisfactory design, construction not according to design, or poor execution of work not covered by standards and left to the discretion of the constructor.

Equipment installation jobs should be planned, and all critical steps and important verifications identified. Construction and maintenance personnel should be responsible for assuring that planning is done, and that workers assigned to the job understand its critical elements.

Typical construction projects will have a number of field inspectors who check for such items as proper documentation (e.g., latest copies of construction drawings), use of proper tools, cleanliness of equipment, and use of proper materials (e.g., gaskets, bolts, welding rods). For projects involving PMI requirements, additional control of materials of construction is necessary.

8.6 Preventive Maintenance

Within the process safety management system, preventive maintenance (PM) consists of a program of tests and inspections conducted on equipment to detect impending or minor failures and to mitigate their potential before they can develop into more serious failures. From a process safety point of view, a PM program consists of a number of activities, including:

- Identification of equipment and instrumentation critical to process safety,
- Determination of required tests or inspections,
- Determination of test or inspection frequency,
- Establishment of maintenance procedures,
- Training of maintenance personnel,
- Development of acceptable limits or criteria for passing,
- Documentation of results.
- Analysis of results

Examples of some common preventive/maintenance activities are listed in Table 8-1.

The first planning step is to compile a list of equipment for which some form of preventive maintenance is desirable. Items may be put on PM because of legal or insurance underwriter requirements, recommended practices by trade organizations, manufacturers' recommendations, company policy, or the facility's determination that the equipment or instrumentation is critical to maintaining the safety of the facility.

Table 8-1
Examples of Preventive Maintenance Activities

- Replace or reset relief valves
- Replace seals on safety-critical pumps
- Measure wall thickness of pressure vessels and critical piping
- Test process shutdowns and other critical instrumentation
- Function-test emergency isolation or vent valves
- Replace rupture discs and flexible hoses

A procedure should also be developed to ensure that new or modified equipment is added to the PM program as appropriate. (This can often be done through the capital project review system or process change procedure.) Figure 8-2 is an example of a PM work request system.

The next step is to select the required test or inspection method; it can range from a simple visual inspection to use of sophisticated tools. Because selection of a method may involve complex technical issues, appropriate expertise should be employed in program development.

Testing should be performed at an established frequency based on known failure history, manufacturer's recommendations, and/or legal requirements (see Section 8.2, Reliability Engineering, and Reference 14). Where data are not available, engineering judgment must be used to set the initial frequency; this rate is adjusted on the basis of actual test data. The management system should also include mechanisms for initiating PM actions at the scheduled frequency and documenting the results.

Control mechanisms should be established to ensure that the required PM has been properly performed. Appropriate maintenance procedures must be developed and approved to ensure that tests and inspections are carried out properly and consistently between individuals. For detailed procedures, checklists should be developed. At the same time, appropriate training must be provided maintenance personnel, so that they fully understand the PM procedures and are qualified to use any special tools or equipment. Coordination with purchasing personnel is also important to ensure an adequate supply of spare parts and the availability of contractors (e.g., for relief valve testing).

The final steps in a PM program include data review and analysis. For each piece of equipment or instrument undergoing PM, a set of criteria should be established to determine if the component has passed or failed the test. If it fails, then appropriate corrective action needs to be specified, including possible replacement. Finally, based on the results of the PM program, testing and inspection frequencies may need to be adjusted.

8.7 Process, Hardware, and Systems Inspections and Testing

Prior to commissioning a new process, replacing equipment, or restarting after a shutdown, a pre-startup safety review should be conducted. The pre-startup review is

Date Issued 1	Required Completion Date 2	Maintenance Authorization No. 3
03/24/80	03/28/80	

Job No. 4	Freq. Code 5	Assigned Supervisor 6	Labor Account 7	Materials Account 8	Related Form No. 9	Related Procedure No. 10
302	011	Inst./Elec.	061-20	056-00	T-LNG-24	11

Job Instructions: **11**

Check batteries with hydrometer. Check battery cables. Submit form on specific gravity. Trickle charge voltage and water level. Keep records of water added to each cell on form and put info on form at 4-month intervals. First Monday of each month, switch charger A to one-hour overcharge. The voltage at end of overcharge should not exceed 2.33 volts per cell.

Equipment Identification **12**

UPS batteries — 12 Each
Turbine control batteries — 12 Each
Emergency generator batteries — 2 Each
Rewater pump batteries — 8 Each

13

Comments:____

Classification 14	Hours	Work Assigned to: 15	Work Permits Required 16	Lock and Tag Required 18	Operations Supervisor Approval to Start 19
Sr. Technician			☐ Yes ☐ No	Electrical ☐ Yes ☐ No	Date
Technician "A"					Acknowledgment Work Complete 20
Technician "B"					1st Oper. Supv. ______
Plantman "A"			Priority 17	Valve ☐ Yes ☐ No	2nd Oper. Supv. ______
Plantman "B"					3rd Oper. Supv. ______
Plantman					4th Oper. Supv. ______
Other					5th Oper. Supv. ______

Approval Maint. Supt. 21	Date	Approval Oper. Supt. 22	Date	Final Inspection By 23	By 24	By 25
				Date	Date	Date

Figure 8–2. *Example of Preventive Maintenance Work Request Form*

a final check of both the equipment and operating procedures to assure that all elements are in place and functional. The review team should verify that all safety items identified in prior design and hazard reviews have been adequately addressed; that operating, maintenance, and emergency procedures have been written; that operator training is complete; that a PM program is in place; that all equipment falling under the PM program has been identified; and that a system for managing change is in place. The latest revision of the piping and instrument drawings should be reviewed, followed by a field inspection. The review team should consist of representatives from design, production, construction, maintenance, and any others as appropriate. The pre-startup safety review is discussed in Chapter 5. This section focuses on the field inspection.

The field inspection provides insights into the design and operation of the equipment that may not be apparent from a review of the drawings. To assure that all issues are considered, a checklist should be used during the field inspection. The checklist should cover such issues as:

- Protection of small-bore lines and fittings from external impact,
- Adequate support of piping,
- Location and identification of critical safety systems and equipment (e.g., area monitors), emergency shutdowns, fire protection equipment, safety showers, and breathing apparatus),
- Location of vents and drains,
- Means of safe egress from an area in case of emergency,
- Means of access to valves,
- Proper electrical classification,
- Proper operation of critical alarm, interlock, and emergency shutdown systems,
- Test and test results from prestartup checks.

The inspection should be made by staff familiar with the design as well as staff familiar with operations. During the inspection, one individual should be assigned to document all items found by the inspection team. The resulting list of items should be prioritized to identify which items must be corrected prior to commissioning, prior to startup, or those that can be corrected at a later time. Appropriate controls should be in place to verify that all items are completed at the required times, and may include another field inspection.

There should be procedures for the testing of key pieces of equipment prior to the introduction of hazardous materials into the process. Testing requirements should be described in startup procedures, and responsibility for completing these tests should be assigned. Completion of equipment tests should be documented with records of the startup.

Upon completion of the review, the team should issue a report identifying any deficiencies that must be corrected prior to startup. Based on this report, a team of plant management staff should be made responsible for approving the facilities for startup. A completed sign-off sheet by all these individuals should be the final document to allow hazardous materials into the process.

8.8 Maintenance Procedures

In performing repair or preventive maintenance work, hazardous conditions may result if the equipment has not been prepared for the job, or if the job is not performed properly. There must be assurance that the equipment is safe to work on. A management system is needed to control the implementation of required maintenance safety procedures.

Any maintenance, whether an actual repair or preventive in nature, should be initiated through a formal system. A written order system is often used to document the work to be done and to facilitate management control of maintenance work. (Figure 8-3 shows one company's form.) A system for organizing the priority of work requests should be adopted, with work requests that have safety implications (e.g., critical instrumentation) given special priority.

Where special precautions are needed to perform the work safely, they should be identified on the work order. Certain types of work may require special work permits (see Figure 8-4), such as:

- Line break (e.g., opening of process line),
- Hot work (e.g., use of open flames or spark-producing tools),
- Confined space (e.g., work inside of process vessels),
- Excavation (e.g., digging).

Each permit should have a set of procedures that defines the requirements under which the permit is issued. The permit should be issued by authorized, qualified personnel with this responsibility clearly assigned. The authorizing person should sign the permits to promote accountability. The management system should address how responsibility will be transferred between shifts when the work extends beyond the time when the original maintenance crew leaves.

A set of safe work practices should be developed to support the work request system. These practices should include:

- Equipment isolation or locking and tagging,
- Plugging or capping open-ended valves,
- Lifting of equipment over active process lines,
- Confined space entry procedures.

After maintenance has completed the work, a final check should be required by qualified operations personnel as a control to ensure that the work requested has been satisfactorily completed, and that all equipment has been returned to an operable condition. Assurance of quality should include ensuring that the proper spare parts are used and that the work performed meets applicable standards and codes.

8.9 Alarm and Instrument Management

Instruments and alarms are vital components to communicate to the operator whether the process is in or out of control. During normal operation, many instruments and alarms are in service and their functionality can be easily verified. Other alarm

1 Dept. Request No.________	
2 Maint. Auth. No.________	
3 Labor Acct. No.________	
4 Material Acct. No.________	

Date Written **5**	Date Required **6**	Estimate Cost ☐ **8**
		Keep Manhours ☐ **9**
Subject________ **7**		Equipment No. **10**

11

Work Requested________

12

Repairs made, parts used, and comments:________

Classification	Hours	Work Assigned to:	Work Permits Required	Lock and Tag Required	Operations Supervisor Approval to Start **18**
Sr. Technician		**14**	**15**	**17**	Date
Technician "A"			☐ Yes ☐ No	Electrical ☐ Yes ☐ No	Acknowledgment Work Complete **19**
Technician "B"					1st Oper. Supv. ________
Plantman "A"			Priority **16**	Valve ☐ Yes ☐ No	2nd Oper. Supv. ________
Plantman "B"					3rd Oper. Supv. ________
Plantman					4th Oper. Supv. ________
Other **13**					5th Oper. Supv. ________

Approval Maint. Supt. **20**	Date	Approval Oper. Supt. **21**	Date	Final Inspection By **22**	By **23**	By **24**
				Date	Date	Date

Figure 8–3. *Work Request Form*

WORK PERMIT

ALL PERMITS VALID FOR ONLY ONE SHIFT AND MUST BE EXECUTED ON THAT SHIFT PRIOR TO STARTING WORK

MINIMUM REQUIREMENTS

LINE OPENING

- ☐ CLEARLY DEFINE SCOPE OF JOB.
- ☐ LOCK OUT ELECTRICAL EQUIPMENT.
- ☐ CHECK LINES FOR CONNECTIONS.
- ☐ LOCK AND TAG.
- ☐ BARRICADE AND POST PROPER SIGNS.
- ☐ TEST SAFETY SHOWER.
- ☐ PROVIDE STANDBY.
- ☐ PUT ON SAFETY PROTECTIVE EQUIPMENT.
- ☐ CLEAN THE EQUIPMENT.
- ☐ WASH PROTECTIVE EQUIPMENT BEFORE REMOVING.

VESSEL ENTRY PERMIT

PERMIT MUST BE COMPLETED BEFORE ENTERING ANY VESSEL FOR INSPECTION OR MAINTENANCE WORK. PERMIT MUST BE DISPLAYED AT VESSEL DURING THE ENTIRE TIME ANYONE IS IN THE VESSEL.

THIS WILL AUTHORIZE THE ______________ MECH. DEPT. / OPER. DEPT.

TO ENTER ______________ EQUIP NAME & NO.

LOCATION ________ BLDG. ________ AREA

FROM ________ A.M./P.M. TO ________ A.M./P.M.

DATE: ______________

PURPOSE OF ENTERING ______________

VENTILATION REQUIRED ______________

- ☐ EXPLOSION METER TESTS RECORDED
- ☐ OXYGEN DEFICIENCY TESTS RECORDED
- ☐ IT IS CLEAN OF FLAMMABLE, CORROSIVE AND TOXIC MATERIALS.
- ☐ CHEMICAL HAZARD TO GUARD AGAINST IS ______________
- ☐ SURROUNDING CONDITIONS ACCEPTABLE FOR SAFE ENTRY.
- ☐ ALL CONNECTING LINES HAVE BEEN BLANKED.
- ☐ LOCK AND TAG COMPLETED.
- ☐ STANDBY MEN INSTRUCTED, FURNISHED AND SIGNED ON LOWER FRONT OF PERMIT SHEET.
- ☐ FALCON ALARM HORN PRESENT AND TESTED.
- ☐ S.H. K-12 REQUIREMENTS REVIEWED AND COMPLIED WITH.

FLAME PERMIT

MINIMUM REQUIREMENTS

- ☐ EXPLOSIMETER TEST RECORDED
- ☐ FIRE EXTINGUISHER PROVIDED
- ☐ COMBUSTIBLE MATERIALS REMOVED.
- ☐ AREA BARRICADED AND PROPER SIGNS POSTED.
- ☐ AREA FREE OF FLAMMABLE LIQUIDS, VAPORS AND DUST.
- ☐ NO SURROUNDING CONDITIONS WHICH COULD RELEASE FLAMMABLES.
- ☐ ALL EQUIPMENT HAS BEEN CLEANED AND INSPECTED.
- ☐ ALL EXPOSED VESSELS FILLED WITH WATER, INERT GAS OR PROTECTED WHERE NECESSARY.
- ☐ ALL PRODUCTION AND MECHANICAL PERSONNEL HAVE BEEN ALERTED.
- ☐ PHYSICAL LIMITS OF THE PERMIT AREA HAVE BEEN SPECIFICALLY DEFINED.
- ☐ I HAVE PERSONALLY INSPECTED THE FLOOR ABOVE AND BELOW AND FIND STATEMENTS NOTED ABOVE CORRECT.

ROOF ENTRY PERMIT

- ☐ CRAFT INVOLVED IN ROOF ENTRY ______________
- ☐ BLDG. ROOF BEING ENTERED ______________

________ A.M./P.M. TO ________ A.M./P.M.

- ☐ DATE: ______________
- ☐ NOTE WIND DIRECTION ______________
- ☐ ARE ADDITIONAL PERMITS REQUIRED FOR ADJACENT BLDG(S). ______________
- ☐ OPERATING SUPERVISION ACKNOWLEDGES ITS RESPONSIBILITY TO IMMEDIATELY ADVISE ALL PERSONNEL ON ROOF OF ANY EMERGENCY.

EXPLOSIMETER TEST

TEST SHALL BE COMPLETED BEFORE AN OPEN FLAME, ARCING, SPARKING OR HEATING DEVICE IS USED.

AREA .... BLDG. ....

LOCATION .... EQUIPMENT ....

DATE ..... TIME ..... READINGS ..... ________ (TESTED BY)

DATE ..... TIME ..... READINGS ..... ________ (TESTED BY)

DATE ..... TIME ..... READINGS ..... ________ (TESTED BY)

DATE ..... TIME ..... READINGS ..... ________ (TESTED BY)

OXYGEN TEST

MINIMUM REQUIRED 20%+

DATE	TIME	READINGS	TESTED BY

I HAVE PERSONALLY INSPECTED AND VERIFIED THAT PERMITS FOR HAVE MET ALL ABOVE REQUIREMENTS

- ☐ VESSEL ENTRY PERMIT
- ☐ FLAME PERMIT
- ☐ ROOF ENTRY
- ☐ LINE OPENING

SHIFT ______________ **DATE** ______________

STANDBY NAMES

1ST .... ☐ MECH. ☐ OPER.

2ND .... ☐ MECH. ☐ OPER.

AUTHORIZATION

OPERATION SUPERVISION	OPERATION SUPERVISION	OPERATION SUPERVISION	OPERATION SUPERVISION
MECHANICAL SUPERVISION	MECHANICAL SUPERVISION	MECHANICAL SUPERVISION	MECHANICAL SUPERVISION

Figure 8-4 Example Work Permit

WORK ORDER NO. | CODE | WORK TITLE

REQUESTED BY | DATE ISSUED | AREA | BUILDING NAME | BLDG. NO. | FLOOR | EQUIP. NO.

APPROVED BY | DATE REQUIRED | DATE COMPLETED | SUPERVISOR | ESTIMATED HOURS

CRAFT	WORK ORDER PERMIT WORK DESCRIPTION	LABOR	MATERIAL

SAFETY PREPARATIONS - CHECK APPLICABLE BOXES

PERSONAL SAFETY

- ☒ SAFETY SHOWER TEST/LOCATION
- ☒ RALLY SPOTS
- ☒ ESCAPE ROUTES
- ☒ EVACUATION INSTRUCTIONS
- ☒ OBSERVE WIND DIRECTION
- ☐ RESPIRATOR REQUIRED
- ☐ COMPLETE ACID SUIT
- ☐ ACID HOOD
- ☐ PROTECTIVE GLOVES
- ☐ FACE SHIELD
- ☐ CHEMICAL GOGGLES
- ☐ SAFETY BELT
- ☐ HEARING PROTECTION
- ☐ VENTILATION REQUIRED
- ☐ TYVEK
- ☐ COMPLETE HOT SUIT
- ☐ USE NON-SPARKING TOOLS
- ☐ NOMEX

CONTRACT ADMINISTRATION

- ☐ DETAILED OCCUPATIONAL HEALTH SPECIFICATION REQUIRED.

CLEAN EQUIPMENT

- ☐ STEAM
- ☐ FILL & DRAIN
- ☐ REMOVE DEPOSITS
- ☐ LEAK INSPECTION
- ☐ VISUAL INSPECTION
- ☐ DECONTAMINATE AND TAG

OTHER ☐

ISOLATE EQUIPMENT

- ☐ STOP TRANSFERS
- ☐ LOCK & TAG
- ☐ DISCONNECT & BLANK
- ☐ POST APPROPRIATE SIGNS
- ☐ ERECT BARRICADE
- ☐ BLOCK ROADWAY
- ☐ RADIOACTIVE MATERIALS
- ☐ CHECK FOR PRESSURE

FIRE SAFETY

- ☐ AREA ALARM NO. ....
- ☐ LOCATION ....
- ☐ STANDBY MAN REQUIRED
- ☐ FIRE EXTINGUISHER LOCATION
- ☐ COVER OPEN TRENCHES & SEWERS
- ☐ WET DOWN FULL AREA

ELECTRICAL SAFETY

- ☐ LOCK & TAG CIRCUITS
- ☐ PULL FUSES
- ☐ DEENERGIZE TRACING
- ☐ EXPLOSION PROOF EQUIP.
- ☐ LOW VOLTAGE LIGHTING REQ
- ☐ SPARK SHIELD
- ☐ GROUND FAULT INTERRUPTER

PERMITS REQUIRED

- ☐ VESSEL ENTRY K-12
- ☐ FLAME K-24
- ☐ ROOF ENTRY K-42
- ☐ LINE OPENING K-33
- ☐ ALARM & INTERLOCK
- ☐ TEMPORARY LINE
- ☐ ELECTRICAL HOT WORK MDP68
- ☐ EXCAVATION K-43
- ☐ SIGN IN-OUT REQUIRED K-31

.... (LOG LOCATION)

OCCUPATIONAL HEALTH

.... (KNOWN/SUSPECTED CONTAMINANTS)

- ☐ AIR SAMPLING
- ☐ SKIN IRRITANT
- ☐ RESPIRATORY IRRITANT
- ☐ CORROSIVE
- ☐ CYANOTIC
- ☐ FLAMMABLE
- ☐ TOXIC
- ☐ ASBESTOS HANDLING MDP60
- ☐ NOISE
- ☐ CARCINOGEN

S.A.F. CODE ....

MEDICAL SURVEILLANCE

- ☐ PRE-WORK URINE
- ☐ POST- WORK URINE
- ☐ UNUSUAL RESTRICTIONS
- ☐ FEMALE EMP. RESTRICTIONS
- ☐ CYANOSIS CONTROL (NEW MAN)
- ☐ MERCURY EXAM
- ☐ LEAD EXAM

THE ABOVE CHECK LIST IS THE MINIMUM SAFETY REQUIREMENTS FOR THE WORK

NOTE: SKETCHES MAY BE ADDED TO CLARIFY

SIGNED: ______________ DATE ______
(WORK LINE UP TEAM MANAGER)

SIGNED: ______________ DATE ______
(WORK LINE UP TEAM MANAGER)

SIGNED: ______________ DATE ______
(WORK LINE UP TEAM MANAGER)

ADDITIONAL INFORMATION

MU-467 REV. 5/88 FIRE: 2222 AMBULANCE: 4000 FUMES: 2222 SPILLS: 3555

systems, however, such as a high-level alarm or any emergency shutdown system, may infrequently, or never, be activated under normal operation, so there is no assurance that it is still functional.

The process safety management system should also assure that other fixed or portable safety-related instruments (e.g., oxygen level detectors) are regularly tested. Such equipment should be calibrated at regular intervals, with management controls in place to initiate the work.

Where these instruments and/or alarms are deemed critical to safe operation, they should be included in the preventive maintenance program (see Section 8.6). Similarly, any instruments or systems containing sensors that are safety-critical and that provide input to computerized control equipment should be included in preventive maintenance programs. Also, any changes to such instrument or alarm settings outside of acceptable ranges should first be reviewed and approved (see Chapter 7).

8.10 Demolition Procedures

Once a piece of equipment is no longer required, appropriate means of isolating and ultimately removing the equipment should be developed. Frequently, a piece of equipment is removed from service for a prolonged period of time prior to demolition. When this occurs, appropriate reviews through process change procedures should be performed (see Chapter 7). If the equipment is definitely no longer needed or usable, it should be scheduled for demolition. Prior to demolition, the equipment must first be isolated from any active equipment in such a way as to minimize piping deadlegs subjected to process pressure. The equipment should be marked in a manner that leaves no question that it is no longer to be used. In such cases, elements of the work request, work permit, and safe work practices should be followed as appropriate.

Decontamination procedures should be developed with consideration for the hazards involved, and these procedures should be thoroughly reviewed. The procedure should address both the decontamination of equipment to be demolished and the related waste disposal issues.

9
Human Factors

9.1 Overview

The term *human factors*, or ergonomics, refers to technical systems and equipment so designed that they can be used safely and efficiently by humans. Human factors is an integral part of many of the other elements discussed in this book; however, since human error plays such a significant role in process safety incidents, effective process safety management should explicitly address human factors.

Ideally, the design and operation of a facility should both anticipate and control the adverse impacts that could result from human actions and human/equipment interactions. Attention to human factors is the mechanism for successfully reaching this ideal. This chapter addresses three significant components associated with this element:

- Operator/process and operator/equipment interfaces,
- Administrative controls versus hardware,
- Human error assessment.

9.2 Operator/Process and Operator/Equipment Interfaces

Anything that increases the difficulty of an operator's job can lead to errors as a result of the shortcuts that the operator may devise. These shortcuts may include improper methods or procedures that may be adequate under normal situations, but are insufficient in upset or abnormal conditions. For example, if the number of tasks an operator must perform is increased, the frequency with which the tasks are done may be decreased to compensate and provide the necessary time. If, for example, this increase involves monitoring additional instruments, no difficulties may arise under routine conditions. However, the increase may significantly reduce the chance that an impending upset will be caught while there is still time to control or avert it. This demonstrates the need for management to assure that human factors are accounted for in all phases of operation.

An effective process safety program includes a commitment to control risks that may arise at two interfaces: (1) the operator and the process, and (2) the operator and the equipment. By incorporating these human/hardware considerations into the process safety program, the chances of incidents caused by human error can be reduced.

The process safety management system should address the operator/hardware interfaces throughout the life cycle of the process. These considerations should be considered in both automated and manually controlled processes.

During the design stages of a process, the company's design standards should require incorporation of human factors principles into the design, instead of simply designing equipment and then motivating and training people to operate it. The various process reviews described in Chapter 5 should explicitly include review of human factors issues. At each stage of the design process, the project manager responsible should be required to explore operator/hardware interface issues, recognizing that the operator is an integral part of the system.

When process changes are made, the systems in place for management of change (see Chapter 7 should explicitly address human/hardware interface issues as a part of the review. Similarly, process safety reviews of existing processes should include examination of human/hardware interface issues.

In operating facilities, there should be mechanisms for obtaining feedback from operators and maintenance mechanics whose first-hand experience will often provide early detection of human/hardware interface concerns or problems. Feedback should be regularly solicited, and then reviewed by staff familiar with operations, engineering, and human factors. The feedback review may be done during regular process safety reviews.

Feedback should be documented and retained. A system should be established to record this feedback in a manner that facilitates periodic trend analyses. Responsibility for maintaining these records and performing the trend analysis should be assigned.

There should also be a program of regular task observation to identify potential human/hardware concerns. Operations personnel should be trained to observe situations where operators have made "ad hoc" modifications to their work stations or equipment. Such modifications often indicate the need for improvement in the human/hardware interface.

When considering the interfaces between operators and the process as a whole, or specific pieces of equipment, one must recognize that there are many types of interfaces possible and many related issues of concern. Table 9-1 presents one listing of the various items that should be included in a comprehensive human factors review. These items recognize that errors may be induced by the nature of the task, the limitations of the operator, the design of the equipment, or the operating environment.

Appropriate resources should be made available for human factors reviews. Both human factors experts and production personnel (including operators) play an important part in effective reviews.

Trade-offs should be considered in implementing human factors-related mitigation measures. For example, changes in design that enhance an operator's job, but that leave limited, poor, or no accessibility for maintenance may not be beneficial from an overall perspective.

9.3 Adminstrative Controls versus Hardware

Administrative controls are the procedural mechanisms (such as standard operating procedures) that are used for hazard control. Hardware controls (such as interlocks) are the controls that are physically built into process systems. In many situations where

Table 9-1
Example Questions for Human Factors Reviews

Operator/Process Interface

- Are display and control channels clearly identified?
- Are computer displays clearly formatted?
- Is operator information clear and accessible?
- Are the implications of actions and their effects clear?
- Are indicators and codes clearly defined?
- Does instrument layout minimize chances of error?

Task Design and Job Organization

- Is operator performance monitored and measured?
- Is operator assistance readily available?
- Is optimum operator activity defined?
- Is there team responsibility?
- Are tne operator's individual responsibilities clearly defined?
- Is there incident follow-up?

Work Place and Working Environment

- Have posture, movement, and accessibility been considered?
- Have environmental conditions (e.g., illumination, noise, temperature, and/or humidity) been considered?

Training

- Are training requirements defined?
- Are training methods developed?

Procedures

- Are procedures concise?
- Are mandatory procedures clearly identified as such?
- Are supporting procedures developed?
- Are operational procedures correct?

---

risk mitigation is desired, a choice can be made among administrative control, hardware controls, or a combination of administrative and hardware controls.

Some of the basic process safety issues involved in the choice are:

- Increased automation (hardware) may simplify the operator's role, but may increase the complexity and frequency of maintenance.
- Operators may rely on alarms to warn of upset potentials and relax their tracking of operations if a system is overly automated.
- Reliance on the operator to take certain actions in emergency situations may not take completely into account fatigue, time to respond, background noise levels obscuring alarms, inadequate numbers or types of communications channels, and the like.

The company should assure that hardware/procedure tradeoffs made by designers and hazard reviewers are based on risk analysis results, and that these decisions are predicated upon past company practice. To encourage consistency and equivalency of risk levels, the management system should encourage communication within the organization on hardware/procedure design practices.

Whenever risk-mitigation measures are being recommended or selected, company practice on administrative versus hardware controls should be considered. This will require a management system in which staff involved in risk control measure selection are familiar with past practice, and in which selections are reviewed by the level of management that approves risk-mitigation measure implementation.

The documentation of risk-mitigation measures selection should record the choices made between administrative and hardware controls. Such documentation will help assure that human factors were considered in selecting mitigating measures, and that there is an "audit trail" for later verification that human factors were considered.

The process safety management system should assure that during capital project reviews, process change reviews, and periodic process risk reviews (see Chapters 5, 7 and 6, respectively), the use of administrative controls and/or hardware controls is explicitly considered. The review forms, guidelines, and/or procedures that are used to manage the review processes should specifically identify human factors, including administrative controls versus hardware, as an issue to be considered.

The process safety management system should assure the availability of human factors knowledge. In some firms, human factors specialists are made available to process safety review teams to bring this expertise to the review. In other cases, human factors training is given to staff involved in process safety review work so they will better understand the issues. Either approach requires the commitment of appropriate resources.

9.4 Human Error Assessment

Even in a perfectly designed situation, operators will still make occasional errors, just as equipment will have failures. Operator errors may be introduced by poor system/equipment design or by the complexity of operations. Human error assessment refers to the determination of human reliability or performance (see Reference 34). As such, it can be used in conjunction with other reliability analyses to determine whether administrative controls to enhance operator performance or hardware changes will provide the greatest improvement in overall reliability/safety.

By conducting human error assessments, one can also obtain a better understanding of whether the human element is performing about as optimally as can be expected, or whether specific design or procedural changes would enhance performance. This evaluation will also make it clearer--in reviewing incidents--as to whether an operator was negligent or conforming to the standards for the job.

Since formal human error assessment is a complex undertaking, it may be useful to have a company guideline indicating when it is to be performed. For example, a process involving very high potential risks and extensive operator control of production might be a candidate.

The initiation of human error assessment should be the responsibility of operating management. However, the conduct of the assessment will require the involvement of specialized experts, or other appropriately trained staff, to fully understand and address the human factors issues.

Various detailed sources are available on conducting human error assessments, as are more generalized data bases on human error rates. While the generalized sources may be adequate for overall reliability analyses, key operations and operator versus automation decisions may warrant or necessitate a human error assessment specific to that particular operation.

In conducting a human error assessment, human factors specialists should be heavily involved. Their analyses should be documented and retained after results are shared with appropriate engineering and operations personnel.

10
Training and Performance

10.1 Overview

Training is an essential part of any process safety management program. The proper training of personnel is an absolute requirement for keeping complex process equipment and machinery on the path to safe operation. This includes making sure that the latest process knowledge is imparted to those responsible for designing, operating, and maintaining the plant. Transmitting the same message to each group tends to reduce the potential for confusion regarding procedures and helps to ensure that consistent actions are taken by all individuals concerned.

As with every other aspect of process safety management, a demonstrated commitment and involvement from the highest levels of management on down is vital to the success of the training function. The well-managed program will have clearly established responsibilities. Furthermore, those who administer the program, design the lessons, develop course materials and tests, as well as those who instruct, monitor, or audit the program, must be accountable for ensuring the adequacy of performance of all who are trained.

Good training is good communication. It does not just tell the student what he is to do, but how--and especially why--it is important to perform each task, and why it must be performed according to established procedures. Good training goes even further by giving the trainee the opportunity to do the required task. By practicing or simulating a task under controlled conditions while explaining the main points to his or her instructor and classmates, most students are much more likely to remember the correct way of doing the job when they encounter it in the workplace.

This chapter discusses the management systems needed for assessing training requirements, defining job descriptions, and determining appropriate hiring qualifications. It also discusses the selection and development of training programs and the qualifications and training of instructors. Finally, it offers insights on measuring performance and the effectiveness of training, and shows how to document and revise a training program.

These issues are discussed within the framework of the CCPS process safety management system components comprising the training element. These components are:

- Definition of skills and knowledge,
- Design of operating and maintenance procedures,
- Initial qualifications assessment,
- Selection and development of training program,
- Measuring performance and effectiveness,
- Instructor program,
- Records management,
- Ongoing performance and refresher training.

10.2 Definition of Skills and Knowledge

A fundamental consideration in planning for process safety training is determining who should receive training and what type of training the individual should receive. The process safety management system should specifically define the skills and knowledge needed for job performance.

Process safety training programs have typically focused on operations personnel, since they have direct responsibility for the plant. However, the training program should be as broad as is necessary to cover needs in all areas of the organization. In planning the training program, consideration should be given to long-term process safety objectives. For example, if enhancing process safety knowledge in plant operations personnel is an objective, the introduction of process safety material into internal management training courses might be considered. Planning should consider the knowledge base that will be developed and accumulated within the firm over a 5- to 10-year period, not just the isolated result of a single training course.

Systematic tools should be used in defining process safety skills and knowledge. These tools help ensure identification of all the training needs for management, first-line supervision, operations, maintenance, and engineering, contractors, safety and emergency personnel and lab technicians who may be present on site. For example, job/task analysis (JTA) is a technique that can be employed to help identify what is important to the safe, efficient and effective performance of any job or task. In JTA, each job is systematically divided into individual tasks or subtasks to a level sufficient to permit determination of the necessary performance requirements, as well as the knowledge, skills, and aptitudes that a worker must have to successfully, reliably, and safely meet the required level of performance. This analytical tool works equally well when evaluating an operating procedure, instructions for disassembly, repair and reassembly of a complex piece of equipment, or determining the performance requirements, skills, and knowledge vital to effective emergency response.

Use of a training matrix, similar to that shown in Figure 10-1, can be helpful in simplifying and tabulating training requirements, including the skill and knowledge levels, needed by an organization.

	Management	First Line Supervisors	Control Room Operators	Field Operators	Material Handlers	Maintenance	QC Lab Technicians	Engineers	Envir. Health & Safety
Plant Safety Organization	1	1	1	1	1	1	1	1	1
Basic Fire Safety	3	1	2	1	1	2	2	3	1
Managerial Responsibilities for Safety	1	1	—	—	—	—	—	2	1
Risk Management	3	3	—	—	—	—	—	3	3
Emergency Management	3	2	3	3	3	3	3	3	2
Hazard Identification	0	2	2	2	2	2	2	1	1
Mathematics	—	—	—	—	—	—	—	3	3
Material Incompatibility	0	2	2	2	1	2	2	2	2
Accident Reporting Procedures	2	2	2	2	2	2	2	2	2
Safe Handling of Toxic Materials	0	1	3	2	1	2	2	2	2
Administrative Control and Approval Procedures for Process Safety	3	1	1	2	2	2	—	3	2

Training Frequency

0 = Initial Appreciation
1 = Annually
2 = Every Two Years
3 = Every Three Years

Figure 10–1. *Example Training Matrix*

10.3 Design of Operating and Maintenance Procedures

As described in Chapters 4, 5, and 7, the design, development, and change of processes should all prompt development of operating and maintenance procedures. Procedures play an important part in defining job requirements, and are also helpful tools for training employees in their responsibilities.

Operating and maintenance procedures both document the steps involved in proper job performance and provide a basis for training. The process safety management system should ensure that procedures are clear and understandable. There should be mechanisms to initiate periodic review, revision, and recertification of procedures by operating and other appropriate personnel.

From operating and maintenance procedures, job descriptions can be developed. Job descriptions are an important planning and organizing tool. When written correctly, they provide a summary of what performance is expected of an employee to ensure that he or she contributes appropriately to the safe and efficient operation of the plant.

The job description, in addition to listing duties, responsibilities, and reporting relationships, also facilitates management control over personnel performance and training program relevance by including the major performance factors, specific skills, and knowledge identified as significant during the training assessment. When a job description is prepared, note the key words and phrases that are used, e.g., follow directions, read instruments, accurately record, adjust, manipulate, and according to written procedures. These are the kinds of expressions that describe the performance, skills, and knowledge aspects of the job while at the same time describing the actual position. Job descriptions need to be reviewed periodically and anytime a major change in duties or performance requirements occurs.

10.4 Initial Qualifications Assessment

Job performance factors, skills, and knowledge requirements play a major role in specifying hiring qualifications. By carefully reviewing the learning objectives for initial training for a given job, an assessment can be made as to what level of relevant skills and knowledge will provide a reasonable starting point for training a new hire in that job. Training professionals and personnel specialists should be intimately involved in determining the appropriate experience and education requirements for each job. Involving supervisors and managers who have experience in the specific area, such as maintenance or operations, will also help ensure a valid assessment.

Some types of testing and evaluation materials can also be used to assess whether a particular job applicant has the right level of knowledge and suitable aptitudes for the job. Such tests should be carefully developed and reviewed to ensure that they contain no bias that might violate Equal Employment regulations. To help ensure that the program remains effective, hiring qualifications should be reviewed periodically, or anytime a major change in duties or performance requirements occurs.

10.5 Selection and Development of Training Programs

The process safety management system should ensure selection or development of training programs that will meet specific training plans and objectives. This is most easily done when the training objectives are well defined and explicitly stated.

When a program consistent with training objectives is considered, its administrative characteristics should be reviewed relative to the firm's requirements. Issues such as program length, time structure (e.g., one long session versus four short sessions), pre-requisite knowledge, audio-visual or computer requirements, cost, and instruction methods should all be considered. The acceptability of the program should be judged by a group that includes training professionals, technical specialists, and operations personnel.

When a curriculum design is established and decisions have been made to develop all or parts of the training program, the next step is to begin the implementation of the program by developing the course materials needed to support the learning objectives. This will include such things as:

- Instructor lesson plans,
- Visual aids,
- Special or modified equipment for demonstrations,
- Student texts,
- Simulators,
- Tests,
- Administrative and record-keeping aids.

Requiring the use of a written lesson plan for a training program is a commonly used control mechanism that helps assure quality and consistency. Without a formal plan, important information may be skipped or extraneous information may be introduced. The lesson plan serves as a guide to the trainer and assures covering all the critical points.

10.6 Measuring Performance and Effectiveness

Several program elements need to be evaluated to determine the level of effectiveness of the training provided. First, the performance of the students as a group and individually requires monitoring. Equally important, trainer effectiveness must also be monitored. Finally, total program effectiveness must be assessed.

The management system should include mechanisms for assessing instructor effectiveness. The performance of students is one useful way of determining the effectiveness of an instructor. Establishing a baseline for student knowledge and performance can be extremely helpful in assessing instructor effectiveness. For example, comparing the scores on tests given before and after training is an excellent way of assessing instructor effectiveness. By administering tests before training, the trainer will also have the opportunity to place increased emphasis on those learning objectives where the most improvement is needed. Thus, the trainer can directly improve both his own and his students' performance. There should also be assigned responsibility for assuring that instructors remain current in the subjects they teach.

One measure of total program effectiveness is continual improvement in on-the-job performance. On the average, the number of spills, releases, fires, emergency shutdowns, and other process-related incidents or accidents attributable to operating error should decrease. Therefore, when an incident does occur, the management system should assure that results of the incident investigation are used to update or modify training programs.

Other measures of training program effectiveness include management observation of task performance. Job recertification programs can also be used to track the effectiveness of training.

10.7 Instructor Program

In implementing a training program, a basic question is: Who should do the teaching? Sometimes the technical content of a lesson can be complicated.

Unfortunately, those who have spent their careers becoming technical experts often have not developed presentation skills, nor do they have the inclination to teach. On the other hand, those who have good presentation skills, may not have what many would consider an adequate technical background to teach complex subjects. Therefore, the selection of instructors should be done to explicity identify--and then use--appropriate staff. Teaching should be a high-priority task. The best qualified person is likely to be busy, but should give training priority to effect the desired results. There should be specific criteria for instructor selection, such as skills in the specific subject, interest in the materials to be taught, leadership, and communication skills.

10.8 Records Management

Documentation of a training program can be important for several reasons. In some cases, various regulatory requirements regarding training may apply. However, the most important reason for documentation is to control the program. Documentation facilitates verification of who has been trained and, in some cases, how effective that training has been. In addition, documentation is the key to obtaining and analyzing the feedback that comes from measuring performance.

Documentation of a training program can be split into five distinct areas:

- Information related to conducting the training,
- Information showing on-the-job performance,
- Information about external factors,
- Identified deficiencies in training objectives,
- Recommendations for revision and follow-up on their implementation.

With regard to the actual instruction process, the following information should be maintained:

- Who was instructed,
- What training were they given,
- Who was the instructor,
- When did the training take place,
- What standards were met,
- What regulations if any were satisfied,
- How did the student perform before and after training,
- When is the student to receive retraining?

This information should be compiled by the instructor and retained by a single responsible person at the facility.

10.9 Ongoing Performance and Refresher Training

Information showing on-the-job performance is most conveniently obtained from incident reports and from employee performance evaluations. Systems should be established to share this information with training program planners.

Changes to equipment and systems, changes in procedures and plant rules, and changes in regulations all affect training requirements. The management system should provide links between performance of current procedures and training program planners.

Deficiencies in training objectives may be identified as the result of student feedback during retraining, or feedback from supervisors who may detect a pattern to performance deficiencies in their department. Since the least desirable way to identify the need for revising a training program is through the occurrence of an incident, great care should be taken in planning and organizing the program.

When a revision is necessary, specific recommendations for the change, including how the need was identified, the significance of the correction, and a specific action plan, should be prepared. Documented follow-up is essential to ensure that changes are implemented and prove to be effective.

To help ensure that the documentation is complete and that the program is being administered properly, annual auditing of the program is important. The audit should determine whether:

- Training was timely,
- Any students were missed,
- Training was appropriate,
- The students accomplished the learning objectives,
- Related job performance is satisfactory,
- The program has been adequately documented,
- Any deficiencies requiring revisions exist.

11
Incident Investigation

11.1 Overview

"Incidents" can be defined broadly as unplanned events with undesirable consequences. In the context of process safety, incidents include fires, explosions, releases of toxic or hazardous substances, or sudden releases of energy that result in death, injury, adverse human health effects or environmental or property damage.

"Near misses" can be defined as extraordinary events that could have reasonably resulted in an accident or incident. To some, the definition of "incidents" includes "near misses". Because there are many similarities between "incidents" and "near misses" for the purpose of process safety management, this chapter uses the term "incident" to refer to both types of events.

Incident investigation is the management process by which the underlying causes of incidents are uncovered, and steps are taken to prevent similar incidents. Because the principal purpose of process safety is to prevent incidents, incident investigation is a key element in any effective process safety management system. Each incident should be investigated to the extent necessary to understand its causes and potential consequences, and to determine how future incidents can be avoided.

In addition to preventing future incidents, there are other important reasons for conducting incident investigations. In the case of an incident that results in a fatality, or in the hospitalization of five or more employees, under the regulations of the Occupational Safety and Health Act of 1970, the employer must report the event to the nearest OSHA office. To make such a report, at least a preliminary incident investigation will be necessary. In addition, an incident investigation that uncovers causes and leads to corrective action will tend to reassure important constituencies affected, such as the neighboring public, employees, and government officials.

An axiom of incident investigation is that process safety incidents are the result of management system failure. Invariably, some aspect of a process safety management system can be found that, had it functioned properly, could have prevented an incident. The causes of these management system failures can be comprised of some of the specific elements discussed in other chapters, such as design procedures, risk management, management of change, process and equipment integrity, training and performance, human factors, or audits. More generally, these failures can be characterized as breakdowns in planning, organizing, implementing, or controlling. Of course, many causes of incidents can be attributed not to management system failures, but to specific technical or human failures, such as equipment breakdown or operator error. However, experienced incident investigators know that such specific failures are but the immediate causes of an incident, and that underlying each such immediate cause is a management system failure, such as faulty design or inadequate training. It is from identifying the underlying causes that the most benefit is gained. This is because by addressing the *immediate* cause, one only prevents the identical incident from occurring again; by addressing the *underlying* cause, one prevents numerous other similar incidents from occurring.

Similarly, it is a rare situation where an "Act of God," or other uncontrollable event, is the sole cause of an incident. Much more common is the situation where an incident is the result of multiple causes, including management system failures. Managers can control the functioning of management systems even if they cannot control the weather. Therefore, it is more appropriate to presume that management system failures underlie every incident so that we may act to uncover such failures and then modify the appropriate management systems, rather than to presume that if an "Act of God" appears to be the immediate cause, investigation should cease because there is nothing that can be done to prevent such future incidents.

In light of the important function of incident investigations in identifying and correcting process safety management system failures, incidents should be looked at as opportunities to improve management systems, rather than as opportunities to assign blame. The cooperation of employees is essential to an effective incident investigation. If the focus of an investigation is to attribute blame, then incidents may not be reported at all, or critical facts may be withheld. What is not reported cannot be investigated, and what is reported incorrectly can mislead or obstruct an effective investigation. Incidents are situations where a careful balance must be struck between upholding accountability and preventing future incidents. The incident investigation should focus on the search for facts. The investigation should be separate from any disciplinary considerations. The investigation process and the investigation team members should clearly and unambiguously deal with all involved individuals in a fair, open, and consistent manner.

The "incident investigation" components are:

- Major incidents,
- Third-party participation,
- Follow-up and resolution,
- Communication,
- Incident recording, reporting and analysis,
- Near-miss reporting,

A discussion of each of the specific components of the "incident investigation" element follows.

11.2 Major Incidents

"Major incidents" are defined, for this discussion, as incidents that result in death, serious injury, serious adverse human health effects, substantial property damage, or environmental damage. Different companies have different criteria for what amounts to "substantial property damage". For example, some companies include incidents that result in adverse publicity within the definition. Each company must select the criteria that are appropriate to its own circumstances. While it is important to investigate all incidents, as the lessons learned in preventing future incidents are not at all related to the magnitude of the occurrence, it is unquestionable that, at the very least, "major incidents" should be investigated. Major incidents carry with them a pall of public mistrust and employee anxiety, which an effective incident investigation can substantially dispel.

Planning and organizing for incident investigations should take place before the incident occurs. This is as much true at a company's headquarters as it is at the facility level. Clear goals and objectives of an incident investigation should be set. Incident investigation procedures should be established to achieve these goals and objectives. Potentially necessary technical resources should be identified and made readily available. The roles and responsibilities of the investigation team should be assigned.

The criteria upon which incidents will be investigated should be clear and known to all employees. A mechanism for reporting the occurrence of an incident should be in place so as to trigger an investigation. Figure 11-1, "Summary Report of a Serious Process Incident," shows an example of one firm's reporting procedure.

An incident investigation team should be organized in a manner that will promote the most effective investigation. The necessary technical skills (e.g., operations, process engineering, metallurgy, chemistry, etc.) should be identified, appropriate lines of authority established, and roles and responsibilities assigned. The need for consideration of third-party participation is discussed in Section 11.4.

Incident investigation procedures are implemented by following a problem-solving process. This process involves gathering the information needed to solve the problem of causation and to reach conclusions. Care should be taken to preserve evidence, pursue unlikely sources of information, and record all the facts. The information is then analyzed with a view to determining the underlying causes of the incident. Appendix C gives an example of one approach to incident investigation.

As discussed in Section 11.1, it is not enough merely to identify the immediate cause of an incident. For example, the immediate cause of the noted 1974 explosion at the Nypro plant in Flixborough could have been the ignition of a quantity of hydrocarbon. If an investigation had stopped once it identified this immediate cause, then nothing would have been learned from this event that would have prevented future incidents. It was necessary to ask why a quantity of hydrocarbon was ignited. It was later discovered that a temporary pipe had ruptured, allowing release of the hydrocarbon. It was *then* necessary to ask why this equipment had failed. It was discovered that the pipe was not suitable for the purpose for which it was employed and that no safety review by a person capable of understanding the hazard had been conducted. It was *then* necessary to ask why no such safety review had been conducted. It was discovered that no system for safety review of design or maintenance modifications was in place. Once this *underlying* cause was uncovered and widely understood, many companies implemented process safety systems for management of change.

These systems have vastly improved process safety over the years following the Flixborough incident, and it is likely that many similar incidents have been prevented.

INCIDENT DESCRIPTION

1. Plant	Date & Time of Incident ☐ A.M. ☐ P.M.	Classification (Note any which apply)
Process Unit/Plant Area	First Reported Date To	☐ Environmental Release ☐ Storage Failure ☐ Fire ☐ Piping Failure ☐ Explosion ☐ Other ☐ Implosion ☐ Near Miss
Equipment Involved		

2. What was occurring in the process when the incident occurred?
(Be specific, describe what materials were being used, how they were being acted upon, or what was being done when the incident occurred.)

Are there safety rules applying to this procedure? ☐ Yes ☐ No Were they followed? ☐ Yes ☐ No

3. How did the incident occur?
(Describe fully the events which resulted in the incident. Tell what happened and how it happened. Name any objects or substances involved and tell how they were involved. Give details on factors which led or contributed to the incident.)

4. Where possible, describe temporary or permanent effects of the incident.
(e.g.: brief gas cloud, damaged piping, ruptured vessel, etc.)

5. How could the incident have been prevented?

6. Date of Report	Report Prepared by	Reviewed by

Figure 11–1. *Summary Report of Serious Process Incident*

INCIDENT PREVENTION (To be filled out by investigative committee)

7. What points were brought out during the investigation?

____

____

____

____

____

____

____

8. What immediate corrective actions were taken?

____

____

____

____

9. Recommendations of action to prevent recurrence | Respon. | Target Date | Compl. Date

____

____

____

____

____

____

____

10. Overall responsibility for follow-up: ______________________

Investigated by (All Team Members): ______________________

____

____

Prepared by: ______________________ Title: ______________________

Distribution:

Figure 11-1 (continued) *Summary Report of Serious Process Incident*

Had the investigation into the cause of this incident stopped at the point at which a specific technical failure had been identified and a recommendation made merely not to use a particular type of pipe for a particular purpose, it is unlikely that the lessons learned by the chemical industry from the Flixborough experience would have been as profound as they were.

An investigation to identify all underlying causes and management system failures should not be limited to major incidents. For example, consider the case where a small quantity of hazardous material is spilled while taking a sample from a process line. It is not enough to look into the situation and conclude that this is an example of an operator error where procedures were not followed, and then simply to recommend that the employee be instructed to follow procedures in the future. Further investigation may reveal deficiencies in the training system. Still further investigation may reveal deficiencies in the management system that plans resources for training or that organizes the training function.

The lessons learned from an incident investigation are limited in usefulness unless they are reported in an appropriate manner. An effective report should set forth a description of the facts, an analysis of the facts which reveals the underlying causes, conclusions to be drawn from the analysis, and recommendations for corrective action. Given the potential for liability arising from major incidents, some companies fear that incident reports will be used against them in court. Organizations should balance the marginal increase in liability risk posed by an incident report against the benefit to be gained by reporting and recording the fruits of the investigation so as to prevent future incidents. The burden on legal defense posed by an investigation report is often minimal because there is a good likelihood of liability in any event. An overriding consideration is the goal of preventing future incidents, and this requires documentation of the investigation results.

To mitigate the potentially negative effects of an incident investigation on liability, some companies have conducted investigations, but have not prepared written reports, or if they have, they have prepared written reports with facts only and no conclusions. This is poor practice because most of the benefit in preventing future incidents is lost if no written investigation report with conclusions is prepared. Many companies involve legal counsel at the outset of litigation. Where an investigation is structured so that it is conducted at the request of legal counsel and reports are addressed to counsel, the level of protection of reports from disclosure in litigation is greatly enhanced. Similarly, it is appropriate for investigation reports to undergo review by legal counsel to ensure that suitable language is used that serves both the needs of preventing future incidents and minimizing legal liability.

11.3 Third-party Participation

Before an investigation begins, the human resources that will be required should be organized. Often a facility at which an incident has occurred will not have certain specialized technical resources (e.g., a metallurgist, an analytical chemist) that may be necessary to fully uncover the causes of an incident. In such cases, technical resources from outside the facility or outside the company may be required.

There may be occasions where organizations should consider staffing an investigation team --at least partially--with personnel from outside the affected facility.

The possibility of bias, lack of objectivity, or the absence of fresh perspectives exists when an investigation team is composed solely of personnel from the facility at which an incident occurred. In addition, management may have greater confidence in the objectivity of an investigation where the team includes clearly unbiased personnel. Some companies have internal facility investigation reports reviewed by an external team. For the same reasons, and particularly in major incident investigations, some companies have employed an independent investigation team from outside the company. This is of particular benefit where there is a need for public credibility in an investigation, such as the context of an anticipated lawsuit.

11.4 Follow-up and Resolution

Implementation of recommendations is a key management task in incident investigations. If follow-up on recommendations does not occur, then the entire investigatory process would have been in vain, and additional liability may be created. Follow-up involves not only addressing specific technical deficiencies at the facility at which an incident took place, but also addressing the applicability of recommendations for process safety management system improvements--both at the affected facility and other similar facilities.

Part of management's planning and organizing function is to ensure that resources are available for follow-up and that accountability is clearly assigned. The follow-up function should involve considering all recommendations, developing and implementing action plans for the recommendations to be adopted, and documenting the basis for rejection or change of recommendations that are not to be adopted. Providing a clear "paper trail" documenting the firm's actions is important to demonstrate due diligence.

Management's controlling function is to ensure that a system is in place to verify that corrective action has been taken. Establishing schedules for the implementation of mitigating measures and tracking progress against these schedules is a common method of control. It is also common to require periodic (e.g., quarterly) written status reports on the progress of corrective action implementation. When implementation is complete, an audit may be performed to assure that corrective actions were implemented as intended. Additional follow-up after a period of time helps assure that corrective measures remain in place.

Clear procedures should be established to address the distribution of incident reports. Reports should be distributed to those involved in initiating and monitoring follow-up. Summaries of these reports, or copies of the full reports, should be distributed to others who have similar processes within the organization and to other professionals involved in process safety management.

11.5 Communication

Because incident investigations uncover management system deficiencies for which corrective action is feasible, the lessons learned from one facility's incident often have applicability to other facilities within a company. A mechanism should be in place to ensure that the understanding of lessons learned is not isolated to one location. The process safety management system should prompt identification of the locations that could fruitfully apply lessons learned from another facility's incident and to communicate these lessons. In some decentralized companies, this is accomplished by cross-divisional committees that exist to share safety knowledge and coordinate efforts. If no such committees exist, then decentralized companies may wish to consider appointing a person with accountability for knowing the needs and requirements of the various facilities within a company and communicating lessons learned.

11.6 Incident Recording, Reporting, and Analysis

Creating an historical record of incidents that is widely available and in a usable form is an important part of a process safety management system. This record could include not only information about major incidents, but all incidents, including near-misses. The record should be in a usable form so that commonalities between past events and potential future events can be brought to light. Relevant categories should be established so that searches can focus on commonalities. Examples of such categories could include specific management system deficiencies (e.g., design, training, safety review, process integrity), hazard sources (e.g., toxicity, explosiveness, ignition sources, weather), immediate causes, process information, and short incident descriptions. The information should be general enough to ensure that an incident is not regarded as an isolated phenomenon, and specific enough to ensure that information is not regarded as too vague and broad to be useful.

Historical incident recording in useful form can allow precautions to be taken at other facilities, allow lessons learned to be taken into account in future design, and help identify trends not apparent from single incidents. Because incidents have many causes,

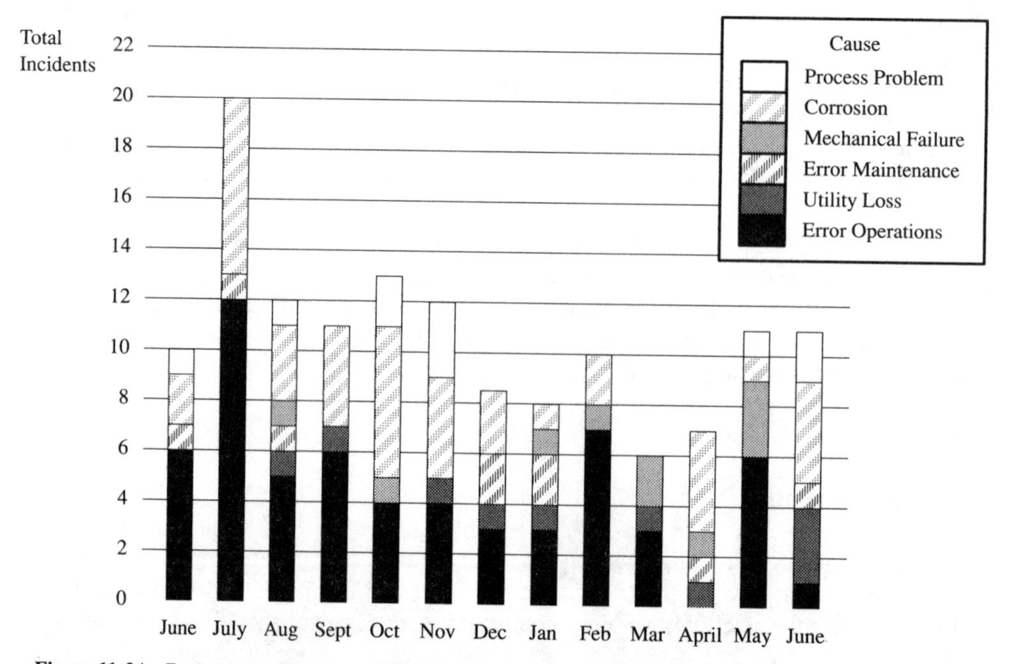

Figure 11-2A. *Environmental Incidents/Spills Trends and Causes—1988/1989 Incident Count*

some causes may not be identified in the investigation of a single incident. For example, if an incident occurs on a Saturday, this may simply be coincidence, or it may be a symptom of deficiencies in management systems on weekend shifts. If a pattern of weekend incidents develops, then management can take appropriate action. Without incident recording and analysis of the record, such patterns may go unnoticed and lessons from which to improve process safety management may go unlearned. Figures 11-2A and 11-2B shows two examples of summary historical analyses.

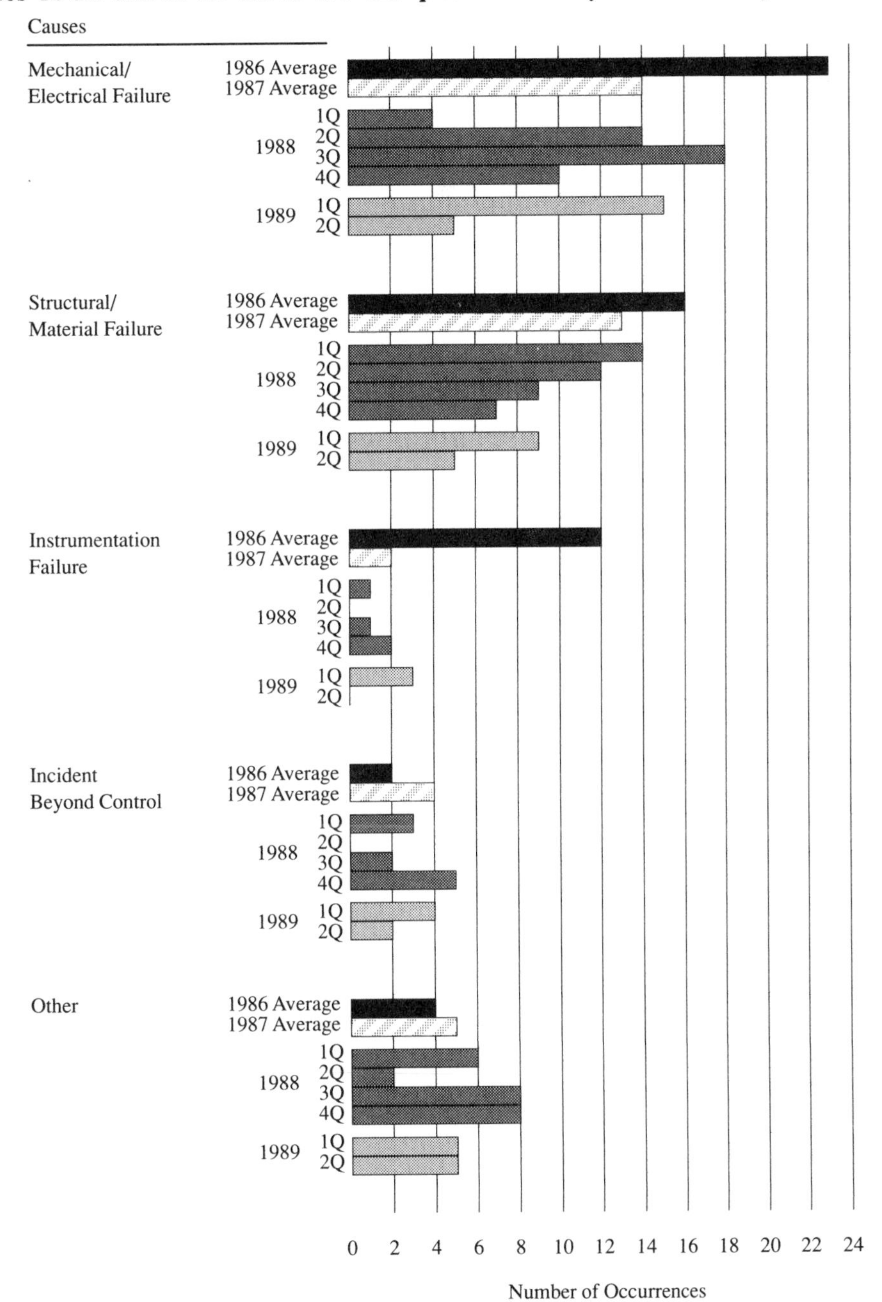

Figure 11-2B. *Reportable Incidents, Cause of Incidents (April 1, 1986 to June 30, 1989)*

11.7 Near-miss Reporting

It is important to note that the same causes and modes of failure are present in both major incidents and near-misses. This means that as many lessons can be learned from near-misses as any other kind of incident. The circumstances surrounding all near-misses should be reported and recorded. While it may not be feasible to investigate every near-miss in the same depth as major incidents, at least some near-misses merit substantial investigation.

Reporting of near-misses is necessary so that a decision can be made as to the depth of investigation needed. As in the case of incident reporting, management should create an atmosphere in which near-miss reporting is encouraged, rather than seen as an opportunity to assign blame. Near-misses should then be analyzed to explore ways in which process safety management systems can be improved. Recording of near-misses allows lessons learned to be preserved for future benefit.

12
Company Standards, Codes and Regulations

12.1 Overview

The goal of company standards, codes, and regulations is (1) to communicate the firm's intentions regarding minimum acceptable safe practice, and (2) to assure that all operating locations within the firm share a common approach to process safety. Codifying such expectations in internal standards helps produce consistent performance among operating locations.

Proper management of standards, codes, and regulations is a necessary part of chemical process safety activities. All U.S. chemical plants, now and in the future, will be subject to Federal Government regulations, such as OSHA 1910 and EPA SARA Title III. Depending on plant locations, state environmental and toxic hazard legislation will also apply. Similarly, plant design engineers need to have access to up-to-date standards and codes to perform their duties in a responsible manner.

In addition to governmental and other "external" standards, many companies develop and implement their own internal standards or guidelines. These internal standards assure a consistency in decision-making by design engineers and plant personnel.

This chapter provides guidelines for the management of both internal standards and external codes and practices, as well as regulations.

12.2 External Codes/Regulations

Many external codes/standards and regulations apply to the layout, design, and operation of chemical plants, and the protection of equipment, employees, and the public. A selected list of some of the general codes/standards and regulations that are generic to most facilities is provided in Table 12-1. A more comprehensive list of general design codes can be found in References 48 and 49.

Planning for the use of external codes and standards involves deciding which codes, standards, and guidelines are to be followed. This decision should be made based on knowledgeable consideration of the firm's processes, equipment, and policies.

Table 12-1
External Codes/Regulations:
Selected U.S. Examples

Organization	*Code/Standard/Regulation*
American Society of Mechanical Engineers	Boiler and Pressure Vessel Code
	Code for Pressure Piping (B31)
American Petroleum Institute	Std. 650 Welded Steel Storage Tanks
	RP 520/521 Pressure Relieving Systems
American National Standards Institute	B31 Pressure Piping
National Fire Prevention Association	Std. 30 Flammable and Combustibles Liquids Code
	Std. 70 National Electrical Code
American Institute of Chemical Engineers	DIERS Procedure for Emergency Vent Sizing
Tubular Exchanger Manufacturers Association	TEMA Standards
Instrument Society of America	Standards and Practices for Instrumentation
Occupational Safety and Health Administration	29 CFR 1910
U.S. Environmental Protection Agency	40 CFR 350/355/370/372 (SARA)
U.S. Department of Transportation	49 CFR transportation

There should be clear documentation of which codes, standards, and guidelines are to be followed, so that everyone involved in design and maintenance clearly knows which guidelines apply. A variance procedure should be established to handle instances where specific local conditions necessitate deviation from accepted standards.

In some cases, operating or engineering personnel may wish to meet the objectives of a code or standard in a way other than that specified by the code or standard. Where this is an attractive option, the location seeking to use alternative approaches should be required to demonstrate that their approach is at least as safe as the applicable code or standard already specified. Approval to use the alternative approach should occur through the variance procedure, with thorough documentation retained.

It is also necessary to organize responsibility for maintaining up-to-date compilations of the applicable codes, standards, and regulations. What information is to be retained and at what level or location in the organization it is to be kept should be clear. For example, Table 12-2 presents a sample plan for organizing such information.

Table 12-2
Sample Plan for
Repository of External Codes/Regulations

Codes/Regulations Information Category	*Corporate Environmental/ Risk Dept.*	*Business/ Technology Center*	*Plant Site*	
			Technical	*Safety*
Equipment & Piping Design	-	C	S	-
Fire & Safety System Design	S	C	C	S
Testing/Inspection Practices	S	C	S	S
Federal Government				
Air/Water Pollution	C	S	S	S
Hazardous Waste/Toxic Substance	C	S	S	S
Occupational Health/Safety	C	S	S	C
Product Safety	C	-	-	S
Transportation Safety	C	C	S	S
State Government				
Air/Water Pollution	C	S		C
Hazardous Waste/Toxic Sub	C	S		C
Fire Codes	C	C		C
Local Government				
Municipal Waste Treatment	-	S		C
Building Codes	-	S		C
CAFR	C	-		C
Fire Codes	-	S		C

Notes:

C = complete copy of codes/regulations
S = selected codes/regulations or applicable sections

Implementation should include keeping the information current and providing notification of new requirements and modifications. Each group with responsibility for archiving the complete documents on a particular standard should make sure that copies of the most recent edition of codes or amendments to regulations are on file. When new regulations or substantive changes to codes are made, the responsible group should issue a news bulletin that alerts other parts of the organization to the changes and informs them how they can obtain revised copies of the documents.

To facilitate use of proper codes, standards, and guidelines, an "evergreen" tabulation of relevant documents under each category should be available. It should cite the names of individuals to contact for obtaining access to recent copies of the information.

Management control of the use of external standards can be handled through an audit. The audit should ascertain whether the latest versions of codes and regulations are available, and whether technical and manufacturing centers are working with the latest editions. Conformance to standards by operating locations should also be verified by the audit.

12.3 Internal Standards

There are some definite benefits in having internally developed standards that complement external codes and design practices. Internal standards allow for the incorporation of actual field experience into the design practices and, as such, they are an embodiment of the company memory, as discussed in Chapter 4. Regardless of the company size, it is desirable to have some internal standards for certain aspects of facility design, especially those unique to the company's processes. The objectives of producing and using internal standards are to achieve consistency in design, where appropriate, and to safely operate and maintain the facilities.

An internal standards program cannot succeed unless it is sponsored by senior management, who either require, or delegate the authority to require, conformance by all operations. Senior management should actively and visibly support the concept of internal standards, and explicitly delegate the responsibility for development of standards and the authority to promulgate them on behalf of the firm.

Internal standards, basic practices, and operating guidelines should be developed and issued for corporate or company-wide adoption and application. One way to achieve this goal is through a centralized technical function, which includes all engineering discipline capabilities, or offers access to them. This function should have responsibility for:

- Assimilation and consolidation of field experience related to equipment design;
- Translation of this experience, coupled with prior knowledge, into safe practices;
- Preparation and peer review of standards documentation;
- Periodic review and upgrading of standards.

Organizationally, this technical function, which offers basic engineering capabilities (chemical, electrical, mechanical, etc.), may report to the technical center manager or the vice president of manufacturing/technology, or an equivalent function. The group with responsibility for standards development should draw on other parts of the organization, such as operations, maintenance, and the like, for review and sign-off on new and revised standards. Process safety expertise should always be involved in the development of safety standards.

Once the standards are developed, they need to be readily accessible and disseminated, understood, and maintained. With the advent of word processing, standards can be compactly stored and retrieved by electronic means, as well as in hard copy. With this increased level of accessibility comes a need for tight control over who is authorized to (1) make changes to the text of the standards, and (2) issue revised disks. Procedures are required to prevent inadvertent use of outdated hard copy.

Technical instruction on the proper use of basic practices is also a necessary element of good management. This is especially true for newly hired or transferred engineers who will be involved in process or project design activities.

Internal standards should not be considered a static document; periodic reviews are needed to incorporate new thoughts and concepts, such as the Design Institute for Emergency Relief Systems (DIERS) approach to emergency vent sizing (see Reference 21). Sections of the basic practices should be reviewed on a rotational basis so that all sections are reviewed within a specified period, such as 5-7 years. The interval for revision of sections should be flexible, and revision should be initiated any time internal incidents, external events, or pressures require.

For firms that do not have an extensive internal technical staff who can be assigned to writing standards, there are other options to consider. For example, some of the major firms that supply raw materials may be willing to share their internal standards for adaptation by a smaller firm. Alternatively, some trade associations (e.g., the Compressed Gas Association) publish recommended standards that can be adopted.

One of the greatest tools for the continuous review of internal standards is a feedback system that encourages constructive criticism. Feedback also provides operating personnel with a greater sense of responsibility for the overall operation.

An audit program (see Chapter 13) should be used to verify that operations are following internal standards.

13
Audits and Corrective Actions

13.1 Overview

This chapter discusses an important element of a program for managing chemical process safety; viz., audits and corrective actions. Audits can be defined as methodical, independent, and typically periodic examinations -- involving analyses, tests, and confirmation -- of local procedures and practices. Audits provide management with a tool for measuring facility performance. The general goal of most process safety audit programs is to verify whether a facility's procedures and practices comply with legal requirements, internal policies, company standards and guidelines, and/or accepted practices. An audit tells a company whether its procedures and practices are adequate, and whether they are being followed.

In addition, today the public, government, company managers, and operating personel want to be assured that an organization is acting as a "good corporate citizen." Audits can help assure that compliance is being achieved with a sound process safety program, and that risks are being appropriately managed.

Beyond playing a significant role as a measurement tool, audits provide the opportunity to share a set of fresh perspectives on areas where requirements have yet to be codified (e.g., process control procedures, management information systems, and maintenance programs). Audits also serve to indicate on-going efforts to re-examine and re-evaluate operations to further reduce operational risks and consequent liabilities (including property damage and business interruption).

Corrective actions, in a general sense, are the steps taken by a company in response to recognition of a process safety deficiency, either through audit findings or other means. Some actions may be taken immediately upon notification of a problem, deficiency, or uncontrolled hazard, while other actions may be longer term and require action planning.

Table 13-1 provides a listing of various reasons why companies have established auditing programs.

Table 13-1
Typical Audit Program Objectives

	Management System Audits	*Compliance Reviews*	*Process Safety Audits*
Help improve overall process safety performance at operating facilities	(x)	x	(x)
Determine and document compliance status with respect to established requirements or criteria	(x)	(x)	x
Increase the overall level of process safety awareness	(x)	(x)	(x)
Accelerate the overall development of process safety management and control systems	x	(x)	(x)
Improve the process safety risk management system	x	x	(x)
Develop a basis for optimizing process safety resource	(x)	(x)	(x)

Legend: x - primary objective
(x) - secondary objective

This chapter describes the components of the audit element of chemical process safety management. These components are:

- Process safety management system audits,
- Process safety audits,
- Compliance reviews,
- Internal/external auditors,
- Corrective actions.

Each of these components is discussed in some detail below.

13.2 Process Safety Management System Audits

Process safety management system audits can be defined as a review of the mechanisms a company has developed to provide increased assurance that its operating units have appropriate systems in place to manage process risks. As such, management system audits examine the operation's process safety make-up: policies and procedures, management organization, planning process, risk assessment and risk management activities and capabilities, management information systems, and internal review/inspection programs.

Process safety management system auditing has been -- and will continue to be -- practiced in different ways by different companies.

Before planning a process safety management system auditing program, the objectives of the program should be identified by senior management. The objectives of audit programs can vary widely, depending on the company's culture, management philosophy, and size. While an audit program may have several basic purposes -- all individually worthwhile -- a single company is not likely to be able to devote its resources to an audit program that would be required to fulfill all or even most of them. Because these program objectives are often competing and conflicting in terms of the role of the audit team, the audit methodology, and the type of audit reporting required, it is important to select audit objectives that are responsive to a firm's organizational needs.

In addition to establishing objectives, audit program planning also involves defining the scope and focus within the context of three separate parameters: specific disciplines/areas, applicable criteria, and locational boundaries.

Different organizations tend to use the audit in different ways. Some view the audit as an important tool for confirming that compliance is being achieved, and that appropriate process safety management systems are in place and functioning. These organizations may favor regular reviews of all key aspects of process safety management at each operating facility. Other companies view a process safety management system audit more as a spot-check activity. In this mode, operating management is expected to take the necessary steps to confirm regularly that appropriate management systems and procedures are in place and being followed. When this is the case, companies typically favor reviews of select aspects of select facilities.

The number of specific disciplines/areas included in the scope of a process safety management systems audit can vary. Any or all of the process safety management elements described in this book can be included. Once the functional areas have been defined, specific audit criteria should be determined. These may be based on a facility's operating procedures, or on generally accepted "good practice".

Selecting the locational boundaries of a process safety management systems audit at a specific site may be complicated. Should the audit include all operations and process units within a facility's property line, then the boundaries are fairly clear-cut. When the audit is limited to specific operating units or processes within a facility, the boundaries may become less clear. Operating units or processes frequently are not functioning in isolation from other units within a facility. The challenge in establishing the audit program is to define the locational boundaries in a way that will fulfill the audit program objectives without spreading limited resources too thinly.

The frequency of process safety management system audits at a facility should be determined by the hazards at each facility. The nature of materials present, facility location vis 'a vis those of its neighbors, and operating history are among the factors that should be considered. Should the decision be made to audit on some cycle, the next step is to determine the length of the cycle.

It may be appropriate to establish different frequencies for different categories of facilities. However, audit program designers and managers should recognize and acknowledge that the complexities of process risk are not easily identified. Thus, when categorizing facilities for audit, it is important to keep in mind that significant problems could arise at a facility perceived to be of a lower risk and thus not selected for high-priority auditing.

As part of planning the audit program, some process should be developed for selecting facilities to be audited. If all facilities are not to be visited on some cycle, a strategy for selecting a sample of the facilities to audit should be developed and documented. Provisions should also be made for responding to special requests from specific locations for audits.

In organizing a process safety management system audit program, several important questions relating to program management and staffing should be answered. They include:

- What are the basic program management responsibilities?
- What criteria should be used in selecting auditors?
- What is the proper use of internal versus external auditors (discussed in Section 13.5.)?

Whether or not a facility has a full-time audit program manger, there are a number of basic program management responsibilities that must be assigned. They include:

- Resource Management. Managing the resources available to the program, including the budget, the personnel, and the other resources available from other parts of the organization;
- Staff Selection and Training. Selecting, orienting, training, and continually developing the audit team staff;
- Program Development. Continuing to develop, refine, and advance the audit program; and
- Keeping Current. Keeping up to date on current activities.

When staffing a process safety management system audit team, it is desirable to have members with expertise in the following areas:

- Facility operations,
- Safety disciplines (e.g., fire protection, electrical hazards),
- Management systems,
- Peer facilities.

The choice of effective team members is important and can ultimately determine program success. To enhance the chance of program success, team members should be chosen for their requisite experience, training, and independence.

The team members should have training and be familiar not only with the program's objectives, but also with the company's established auditing practices and approaches. Team members should be prepared to conduct an audit efficiently and effectively while at the facility. If the audit departs from the firm's established approaches, a variance procedure should be followed to document the deviation, and the deviation should be approved by the manager(s) responsible for the audit program.

Production or operations departments may be chosen at the location of the audit program to reflect and reinforce the company's philosophy that operations are responsible for process safety management. A company's law department would be a logical choice when sensitive legal issues are involved.

The appropriate organizational location of a process safety management system auditing program is basically a question of where the program should be housed to ensure that the right skills, expertise, knowledge, and experience base are brought to bear. The audit program should have sufficient organizational influence to guarantee that the required resources are made available to achieve the program's objectives, and that audit findings will receive serious attention and proper consideration. In addition, the position of the audit program within the organization should be predicated upon the value of the independence of the audit function versus access to and familiarity with information that is to be audited.

By selecting a separate internal audit department to house the process safety management system auditing program, the program may tend to be viewed as a corporate (rather than process safety) management tool. As such, the audit program serves strictly as a double-check on the system, with operating management expected to manage process safety hazards and compliance. If the auditing effort is conducted by individuals who are not part of the day-to-day operating management staff, a truly independent spot-check of the system can be provided.

Most companies prepare a written audit report. The purposes of the report are typically to provide management with information about facility status; to document how the audit was conducted, what it covered, and what was found; and to initiate corrective action.

Some companies prepare a draft of the audit report on site. Most, however, prepare a draft audit report shortly after the on-site audit is completed. This draft usually undergoes review and comment before a final report is issued. Report reviewers may include the process engineering department, law department, facility management, and the audit team.

While much has been written about protecting the confidentiality of the audit report, most well-established programs--especially those that conduct a large number of audits each year--do not routinely take steps to assert the confidentiality of the audit report. Instead, care is taken in preparing the report (1) to assure that the report clearly, accurately, and appropriately reports the facts; and (2) to ensure that timely, appropriate follow-up action occurs on all report items. The audit report is typically treated as an internal management communication and is distributed only to those with a "need to know"; a few companies, however, treat the report as "attorney-client" privileged communication.

13.3 Process Safety and Audits

Process safety audits are intended to provide management with increased assurance that operating facilities and process units have been designed, constructed, operated, and maintained such that the safety and health of employees, customers, communities, and the environment are being properly protected. As such, process safety audits generally check the implementation status of proposed control actions; ensure that critical operating procedures and preventive maintenance procedures are adequate, up to date, and being followed; and ensure that the integrity of original designs is being maintained.

A number of specific aspects or functional areas can be included in the scope of a process safety audit. Usually included are: process materials management; process facilities (e.g., pressure relief, isolation valves, piping systems, flash arresters); process control (e.g., interlocks, instrumentation fail/safe modes, control bypasses, alarms, shutdown systems, computer controls); electrical hazards (hazard classification, grounding); fire protection (availability, completeness, emergency response, updating procedures); and critical operating parameters and operational safety standards.

When staffing a process safety audit, it is desirable to have team members with the following expertise:

- Process engineering/design (control technologies),
- Safety disciplines (fire protection, electrical hazards, material handling),
- Chemistry,
- Facility operations (maintenance and operations),
- Auditing,
- Peer facilities.

Many of the management system considerations for process safety audit programs parallel those for process safety management system audits, as described in Section 13.2.

13.4 Compliance Reviews

Compliance reviews can be defined as the process of confirming that a facility's operations comply with applicable laws and regulations, as well as company policies, procedures, and practices. By its nature, a compliance audit includes a rigorous effort to determine and document performance by evaluating the application of and adherence to applicable process safety standards. Compliance audits can certify the validity of process safety data and reports, and also identify gaps in organizational policies and standards and in the facility's adherence to these standards. In addition, the audit may consider compliance with other parameters, such as industry or association standards. The compliance criteria should be established in the planning phase.

In conducting compliance reviews, an important aspect is confirming the existence and effective use of variance procedures. Such formal procedures should be used whenever deviations are made from established standards, policies, or guidelines.

13.5 Internal/External Auditors

The degree of audit independence that is desired by the person for whom the audit is being conducted will influence the decision on team membership. If an inside independent verification is sufficient, no outsiders need be involved. However, if corporate management or process safety management decide that they would like to have an outsider's view of the performance status of the corporation's facilities, an outside agent will have to become involved. Sometimes external auditors are also sought because of the lack of available in-house expertise.

13.6 Corrective Actions

The corrective action process is closely related to auditing. In some organizations, corrective action is a formal part of the audit program; in most others, corrective action is merely closely linked to the audit process.

Corrective action, broadly defined, includes not only the process of addressing identified deficiencies, weaknesses, or vulnerabilities, but also the processes for corrective action planning and follow-up. Figure 13-1 summarizes the corrective action process and its various components.

The corrective action process typically begins with management consideration of the audit findings and issues, which are usually given in the audit report. The primary purpose of management consideration is to determine what actions (if any) are appropriate or desirable. Other important determinations include corrective action priorities, timetables, resource requirements, and responsibilities. Corrective action planning can include several other dimensions. For example, in some situations, there may be a need for identification and authorization of interim, or stop-gap, measures to provide quick or immediate corrections to, or mitigations of, especially hazardous or significant conditions. There may also be a need to consider similar or related concerns at other locations or units (including those at other companies in situations where technology is licensed or common).

Management review and determination of a particular course of corrective action are especially important when audits include issues or recommendations for areas where established criteria or clear requirements are not available. In such cases, the corrective action process must determine what, if any, action is appropriate, both to achieve the company's process safety objectives and to meet its other business interests.

In some instances, corrective action may simply involve remediation of a condition or situation. However, in many instances, there is also likely to be a

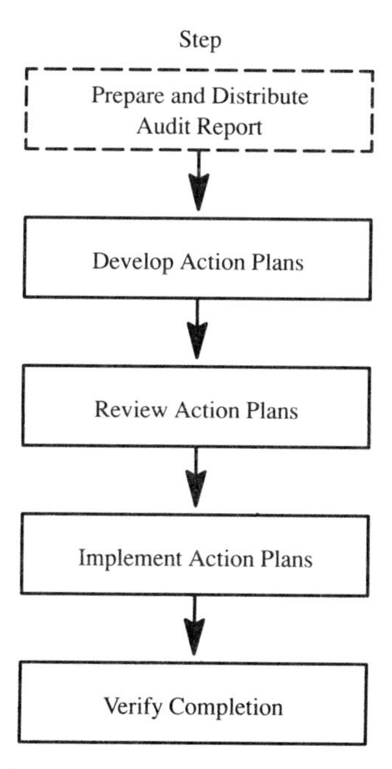

Figure 13–1. *Audit Follow-up Steps*

preventive component of the corrective action. In such instances, the corrective action intends to prevent (or further reduce the likelihood of) recurrence of the undesirable situation.

In some instances, no action may be a valid response to an audit finding. Where this is the case, there should be thorough documentation of why no action is considered necessary.

Because it is important to assure that the deficiencies identified are corrected, a close-out phase of the corrective action process is typically conducted to provide review or assurance of the completion of the actions specified in the action plan. In some instances, this review or assurance is provided by individuals assigned responsibility for completion of the action item or by facility management. In other situations, the audit program may specifically follow up on the status of the agreed-upon actions and confirm their implementation.

To control the corrective action process, many companies make use of a tracking system. To assist in the tracking of corrective actions, a variety of reporting mechanisms can be used, such as:

- Periodic status reports (e.g., quarterly/monthly),
- Milestone reports (summarizing accomplishments),
- Exception reports (other major milestones).

Corrective action tracking provides management with the status of audit issues and agreed-upon corrective actions. It also provides an opportunity, in some cases, to review corrective action at a later date subsequent to completion (e.g., a year later).

14
Enhancement of Process Safety Knowledge

14.1 Overview

The preceding chapters have discussed and given examples of the major elements and components necessary to planning, organizing, implementing, and controlling an effective process safety program. Management commitment to using all available resources for enhancing process safety knowledge at all levels in the organization is a key difference in having a minimum, adequate, or outstanding process safety program.

Process safety is a dynamic field, and these Guidelines should not stifle creativity and innovation. Companies with strong process safety programs should strive to benefit from the latest advances in process safety technology, and keep abreast of technological advances through active participation in professional and trade associations.

Organizations with outstanding programs will be contributing to advancing the state-of-the-art of process safety by sharing non-proprietary results of internal process safety research, and supporting the process safety-oriented research and development programs of professional and trade associations or colleges. They should encourage technical staff participation in professional and trade association programs and provide for the development of process safety reference libraries. Financial grants and active volunteerism are also viable options open to most organizations, regardless of size or resources.

The enhancement of process safety knowledge also provides broader benefits. Improved process knowledge and understanding can produce a competitive advantage, for example, through improved yields, better quality, and increased productivity.

14.2 Professional and Trade Association Programs

Quite a variety of useful process safety programs and resources have been initiated by various professional and trade associations. It is important to know what each organization is doing, where they are involved, and their objectives. Table 14-1 presents a compilation of some of these organizations and the services, programs, and other resources that they make available to managers and their technical staffs for enhancing process safety programs.

Table 14-1
Professional and Industry Organizations Offering
Process Safety Enhancement Resources

Organization	*Selected Examples of Programs Offered*
ACS American Chemical Society 1155 16th St., N.W. Washington, DC 20036 (202) 872-4600	• Chemical Properties Referral Service • Referral to Regulatory Agencies • Chemical Safety Manual for Small Business • Hazard Communication Standard Information • Laboratory Safety and Design Information
AIChE American Institute of Chemical Engineers 345 E. 47th Street New York, NY 10017 (212) 705-7338	• Center for Chemical Process Safety (see Section 14.3) • Design Institute for Emergency Relief Systems (DIERS) • Design Institute for Physical Properties Research (DIPPR) • Loss Prevention Symposia (Health and Safety Section) • Continuing Education Short Courses
AIHA American Industrial Hygiene Association 475 Wolf Ledges Pkwy. Akron, OH 44311 (216) 762-7294	• Emergency Response Planning Guidelines • Workplace Environmental Exposure Level Guides • Hygiene Guides (Toxic Properties Surveys) • Professional Development Seminars • Short Courses at Annual Conferences
ANSI American National Standards Institute 1430 Broadway New York, NY 10018 (212) 354-3300	• Consensus Standards on Various Subjects

Table 14-1 (Continued)

Organization	Activities
APCA Air Pollution Control Association P.O. Box 2861 Pittsburgh, PA 15230 (412) 621-1090	
API American Petroleum Institute 1220 L. St., N.W. Washington, DC 20005 (202) 682-8000	• Process Hazards Management Task Force • Process Hazards and Process Safety Seminars • Technical Standards (Fire Protection, Maintenance) • Equipment Inspection Guides • Operator and Maintenance Training
ASME American Society of Mechnical Engineers 345 E. 47th Street New York, NY 10017 (212) 705-7722	• Pressure Vessel Code • National Board (Repair of Pressure Vessels and Safety Valves) • Non-destructive testing
ASSE American Society of Safety Engineers 1800 E. Oakton Street Des Plaines, IL 60016 (312) 692-4121	• Continuing Safety Education Courses - Introduction to System Safety - Recognition of Accident Potential - Chemistry of Hazardous Materials - Scientific Accident Investigation - Industrial Explosion Prevention • Professional Development - SARA III - Emergency Preparedness - Safety Management (Fundemental and Advanced)
ASTM American Society for Testing and Materials 1916 Race Street Philadelphia, PA 19103-1187 (215) 299-5400	• Waste Compatibility Guide

Table 14-1 (Continued)

CMA Chemical Manufacturers Association 2501 M St., N.W. Washington, DC 20005 (202) 887-1100	• National Chemical Referral and Informational Center (including CHEMTREC) • Community Awareness and Emergency Response (CAER) • Management Guidelines - Process Safety Management Survey - Managers Guide to Quantitative Risk Assessment - Facility Inspection and Safety Program Evaluation
Compressed Gas Association 1235 Jefferson Davis Hwy. Arlington, VA 22202 (703) 979-0900	• Guidelines for Compressed Gas Storage and Handling
FEMA Federal Emergency Management Agency 500 C Street, S.W. Washington, DC 20472 (202) 646-3923	• Handbook of Chemical Hazard Analysis Procedures
HMAC Hazardous Materials Advisory Council 1012 14th St., N.W., Suite 907 Washington, DC 20005 (202) 783-7460	
IChemE The Institution of Chemical Engineers (U.K.) 165-171 Railway Terrace Rugby, Warks CV 21 3HQ (0788) 78214 TX: 311780	• Loss Prevention Bulletin (Case Histories) • Information Exchange • Training Modules • Conference on Major Accident Prevention
IEEE Institute of Electrical/Electronic Engineers 345 E 47th Street New York, NY 10017 (212) 644-7900	• IEEE Transactions on Reliability Special Issues: Chemical Process Reliability Safety and Risk Management

Table 14-1 (Continued)

NAM National Association of Manufacturers 1331 Pennsylvania Ave., N.W. Suite 1500 N Washington, DC 20004 (202) 637-3000	•Case Histories of Accident Causes and Prevention •Computer Analysis of Accidents (NAM Safe System) •Process Hazard Management Standard Review •Process Hazard Task Force •Hazard Training Task Force
NFPA National Fire Protection Association Batterymarch Park Quincy, MA 02269 (617) 770-3000	•Consensus standards related to fire and explosion prevention
NICS National Institute for Chemical Studies 2300 MacCorkle Ave., S.E. Charleston, WV 25304 (304) 346-6264	•Chronic Health Effects Study •Voluntary Reduction of Routine Emissions •Community Safety Assessment Program •Emergency Reponse Database
NSC National Safety Council 444 N. Michigan Avenue Chicago, IL 60611 (312) 527-4800	•Accident Prevention Manual for Industrial Operations •Safety Video Programs - Instruments and Controls - Fire Safety - Hazard Communications - Accident Investigation •Safety Training Institute
SOCMA Synthetic Organic Chemical Manufacturers Association 1330 Connecticut Ave. N.W., Suite 300 Washington, DC (202) 659-0060	•Worker Training and Certification
SPI The Society of the Plastics Industry 355 Lexington Avenue New York, NY 10018 (212) 503-0600	

Table 14-1 (Continued)

SRA Society for Risk Analysis 8000 Westpark Dr., Suite 400 McLean, VA 22102 (703) 790-1745	• Conferences on Risk Analysis
SSS System Safety Society P.O. Box 165 Washington, DC 20044	
World Bank International Bank for Reconstruction and Development 1818 H Street, N.W. Washington, DC 20433 (202) 477-2001	• Manual of Industrial Hazard Techniques • Workshop Procedures Safety Management and Risk Control • Occupational Health and Safety Guidelines

Each organization should decide which professional and trade associations it plans to support, and then designate appropriate personnel to participate in the associations' activities. The time required for active participation should be planned to assure that the firm receives the best value for its participation.

14.3 CCPS Program

In response to public and private concerns and the demand for greater chemical plant safety, the American Institute of Chemical Engineers established the Center for Chemical Process Safety (CCPS). Although CCPS does not enter into any regulatory lobbying efforts, CCPS Guidelines do provide technically sound alternative methods which represent the latest technologies and are accepted good practice in the industry. These may be referenced by regulatory bodies. The technical elements contained in this particular guideline are included in the EPA 305 b Report to Congress which defines what constitutes a sound chemical process safety program.

Many of the larger chemical companies have voluntarily made available to CCPS the knowledge and expertise of experienced process safety engineers, scientists, and managers to produce a series of guideline documents. This book is an example of such guidelines. Both large and small companies now routinely send engineers and managers to CCPS-sponsored conferences which impart the latest information on the prevention and mitigation of major chemical accidents. The number and affiliation of the technical speakers at these events continue to expand as more companies recognize the importance to the success of their own process safety programs of becoming involved in and supporting CCPS activities.

CCPS is also involved in promoting the incorporation of process safety in engineering curricula, and in promoting research in areas where the state-of-the-art can and needs to be advanced.

Participation in CCPS programs should reflect the same management considerations as are noted above for other professional associations.

14.4 Research, Development, Demonstration, and Implementation

There are many important aspects of process safety where additional independent and organized study may be needed. Some key areas include:

- Material properties,
- Fire and explosion hazards testing,
- Reaction kinetics,
- Acute and chronic toxicity,
- Reliable ways to screen for the detonation potential of pure materials and mixtures,
- Emergency relief system design,
- Testing and evaluation of process safety equipment and systems in full-scale pilot plant and controlled operations,
- Failure rate data specific to process conditions.

Management should plan for process safety research and development and provide a budget for the financial and technical resources necessary to support it.

Users groups that sponsor research and share results already exist for several of these areas. The Design Institute for Physical Properties Research (DIPPR) Users Group, and the Design Institute for Emergency Relief Systems (DIERS) Users Group are examples of two AIChE-sponsored programs. The key to the success of such efforts is industry participation. Many companies have made the commitment to encourage regular involvement of key technical personnel in serving on various subcommittees, making presentations, and helping to conduct the business of these volunteer, non-profit organizations.

Research project planning should incorporate the knowledge of design and operations personnel as well as research staff. The results of research should be effectively communicated to all concerned parties and incorporated into internal standards for safe design and operation. This requires assignment of responsibility for assuring that research results are disseminated in a useful form.

14.5 Improved Predictive Systems

Techniques for predicting the likelihood of a hazardous incident, its probable zone of impact, and its most likely effects or consequences upon people, the environment, and property are still evolving. Additional effort to improve predictive systems is still needed to enable engineers to make such calculations with the same confidence and reliability associated with traditional equipment design.

Organizations should identify means of following developments in failure rate data and models, hazard consequence models, and chemical toxicity and reactivity data.

In addition, efforts should be made to learn from one's incident investigations (Chapter 11) and preventive maintenance (Chapter 8). Both can provide information useful in improving predictive systems. The management system should assure that adequate information transfer occurs and that analyses are performed periodically.

14.6 Process Safety Resource Center and Reference Library

Establishing special process safety resource centers is another way to enhance the knowledge of process safety within an organization. Depending upon the size of the organization, one or several such centers may be needed. The information that should be included in such a library ranges from a number of commercially available books, including the CCPS Guideline series, to a customized set of in-house documents which contain process safety-related information needed by engineers and designers, first-line supervisors, and safety supervisors. The in-house collection of documents might include, but should not be limited to, the items listed in Table 14-2.

The process safety resource center will require active oversight to assure that the contents remain up-to-date in this evolving field. The existence of the resource center should be made widely known to all engineers, researchers, and operations personnel.

Table 14-2
Examples of Subjects Covered in Process Safety Libraries

- Accident/incident reports
- Plant equipment design data
- Hardware type and design practices (codes and standards)
- Rules and regulations
- Appropriate sections from the Code of Federal Regulations (CFR)
- A subscription to a legislative and regulatory service consisting of basic text, monthly supplements, and newsletters
- Relevant environmental organization newsletters
- Trade association information
- Chemical data, including properties, reaction kinetics, and safe handling information
- Risk management techniques
- Technical papers
- Case histories concerning incidents that illustrate fundamental process safety principles or lessons with plant-specific application
- News clippings that illustrate the importance of good risk management and communications practice.

15
Conclusion

Prevention of chemical process incidents requires the implementation of effective, comprehensive process safety management. This document has described elements and components of chemical process safety management to assist the reader in understanding the requirements for process safety management systems. Subsequent work by CCPS is planned to provide "how-to" implementation detail on the content of process safety management elements.

The scope of the comprehensive process safety management program is large; however, it is important for designers and managers of process safety management systems to understand the complete context into which each component will ultimately fit. Implementation of process safety management systems is often done in stages, with the components most important to a company's operations addressed first. However, a comprehensive chemical process safety management system must ultimately make provision for addressing each of the components.

Process safety management should be considered as an integrated activity, with appropriate linkages among the various elements and components, rather than as a series of discrete activities. Through this "holistic" approach, process safety can be most effectively managed.

While an integrated approach to process safety is the objective, the reader should not be intimidated by the potential size of the effort involved in designing and implementing a process safety management system. Such systems are usually approached in a phased manner, with managable-sized efforts undertaken. While the objective should be a comprehensive, integrated, process safety management system, each step toward that objective will contribute to the enhancement of process safety performance.

Appendix A
Characteristics of a Management System

For administering any one or all of the technical elements of a chemical process safety program like the one identified in the main body of this document, there are certain characteristics of a management system that should be in place to ensure that the program is carried out efficiently and effectively. These characteristics are sufficiently generic so as to apply to systems for managing virtually any important technical activity; however, they have particular value as a profile of the principal requirements of a management system for chemical process safety. Still, this list is not necessarily definitive. Not all features or characteristics may be needed in every specific company situation. Exceptions and departures based on local circumstances are acceptable. Also, suggested changes and additions are encouraged. They follow:

- Explicit Goals and Objectives. Goals describe the overall, long-range targets that the company seeks to achieve. Objectives translate the goals into more specific statements of purpose, i.e., what it is the company is trying to gain from the activity.

- Well-defined Scope. Each element of a chemical process safety program, if it is to be well managed, requires a clear definition of its component parts or activities. For example, an effective program for incident investigation should have a well-defined means for addressing incident and near-miss recording, internal reporting, external notification, incident follow-up and resolution, and third-party review as needed. The boundaries of these activities need to be clearly understood and widely communicated within the organization.

- Clear-cut Desired Outputs. Wherever possible, planning for individual elements or component parts of a process safety management program should identify specific measures for desired outcomes and set target or desired levels for each. The measures selected should capture the benefits to the company of pursuing the particular activity and express them in terms that clearly communicate to management both the value of that activity and the extent of goal achievement.

- Consideration of Alternative Achievement Mechanisms. Once the questions of what is to be accomplished and how much of it is desired have been answered, it still remains to process safety planners to determine how this will be done.

Planners must be able to identify, evaluate, and ultimately choose among feasible technical and administrative means available to achieve the specified level of program outputs. The key to this process is the early and explicit consideration of alternatives. Different mechanisms for reaching program goals need to be assessed in terms of their efficiency and effectiveness of goal achievement as well as for their "fit" with company culture and values before a preferred approach is selected.

- Well-defined Inputs and Resource Requirements. Sound planning for chemical process safety requires an equal degree of specificity in determining the types and amount of personnel, financial, and technical resources needed to accomplish desired program outputs. These include not just headcount and capital and operating budget dollars, but also specific technical disciplines and skill levels among the available staff. Inputs and resource requirements will differ significantly, depending upon whether the specific activity involves a single project having a finite beginning and end, an ongoing process, or a program made up of multiple processes having extensive feedback loops. In any of these situations, not only must inputs be identified as precisely as outputs, the levels of the two need to be consistent if management goals and objectives are to be achieved.

- Identification of Needed Tools and Training. Carrying out effectively agreed-upon approaches to achieving specific process safety management outputs may require use of specific tools, e.g., diagnostic or measurement equipment, analytical methods, predictive models, and/or sophisticated computing and data management. The planning function must provide for these tools--in the types and quantities needed. It must also identify the specific skills training needs of company employees who will be assigned responsibilities for carrying on particular process safety management activities, including use of specialized tools.

Organizing

- Strong Sponsorship. Each technical element in a process safety management program needs to have a specific person or organizational unit clearly designated as responsible for its design, implementation, and maintenance as well as for seeing to it that it receives proper review. Having this designated "champion" for the activity helps assure that it receives adequate management attention and support. Overall, the process safety management program as a whole requires a strong commitment from senior corporate management. For the program to be effective over the long term, top management should take the opportunity to make frequent clear statements to employees and the public about their personal expectations for the company's process safety performance, and illustrate this commitment by regularly requesting information on the status of company safety activities.

- Clear Lines of Authority. Not all technical elements of a chemical process safety program need report to the same responsible individual, but, collectively, the lines of reporting authority and accountability for the various specific elements should be direct and unambiguous. The organizational structure itself should promote clarity of understanding among all involved as to the chain of command and relevant approval/authorization requirements affecting process safety activities.

- Explicit Assignments of Roles and Responsibilities. A management system for chemical process safety must identify and assign responsibilities for specific activities under each technical element to designated organizational units and individual job titles. These assignments should also be reinforced within the organization through detailed job descriptions, clear measures of job performance, and annual personnel reviews tied to performance factors.

- Formal Procedures. A management system for chemical process safety further organizes and structures the work related to specific technical elements through development and use of formal written procedures. These procedures translate the roles and responsibilities of organizational units and individuals into well defined task sequences for both one-time and ongoing process safety management activities. If followed, they help ensure consistent work performance designed to meet planned process safety objectives and desired outputs.

- Internal Coordination and Communication. Well-designed management systems seek to eliminate organizational barriers to the coordination of process safety-related activities across functional specialty lines, and to actively promote close working relationships among operating, engineering, R&D, safety, legal, and environmental personnel within the company. Organizations characterized by strong formal and informal networks of professionals sharing process safety consensus are frequently better able to identify potential new sources of hazards and to respond to them more quickly and effectively.

Implementing

- Detailed Work Plans. Ongoing activities under specific technical elements of the chemical process safety management program, as well as important new process safety-related projects, should receive detailed management attention to work task identification, planning, staffing, budgeting, scheduling, and review. The benefits of such detailed planning include a sharper focus on obtaining desired safety results and increased management accountability for doing so.

- Specific Milestones for Accomplishments. As an outgrowth of detailed work planning, an effective system for managing the implementation of process safety-related activities and projects also stresses the identification of clear schedule targets for work accomplishment, key points in time when management direction can be asserted to help guide achievement of program objectives and desired outputs. Ongoing activities and special projects alike should be implemented in such a way as to make use of these schedule milestones as important devices for communicating management expectations for specific work performance.

- Initiating Mechanisms. For certain one-time and other non-routine events and activities, a management system for chemical process safety must identify and provide for specific mechanisms that will trigger appropriate administrative actions as needed. Examples include procedures that trigger safety reviews for requested process changes, material substitutions, and major new capital equipment for both variance requests and pre-startup activity on selected types of projects.

Controlling

- Performance Standards and Measurement Methods. Individual technical elements in a chemical process safety management program require establishing standards and criteria for determining acceptable levels of process functioning and work performance, e.g., statistical process control standards, criteria for boiler test/inspection, and equipment preventive maintenance. A management system must specify what these standards are as well as appropriate equipment and/or methodologies for measuring performance against them.

- Checks and Balances. From a process control standpoint, some of the performance standards specified by the management system will be fault tolerances for specific excursions beyond desired ranges for such parameters as temperature, pressure, and level or weight. The process safety management system must also spell out how the process (or processes) has been designed to tolerate faults and to respond appropriately, e.g., systems and procedures for high and low alarms, second alarms, or automatic shutdown. For work performance standards as well, the management system must also provide guidance for acceptable deviations and appropriate response, e.g., how much time should elapse past a required inspection or maintenance activity date before follow-up should be initiated.

- Performance Measurement and Reporting. Using specified performance standards, fault tolerances, and measurement methods, a chemical process safety management system must then provide for appropriate recording (automated or manual) of process/work performance information following well-defined documentation requirements. The system should also address the issue of efficient reporting of this information, e.g., which items at what level of aggregation, to whom, and how frequently.

- Internal Reviews. In conjunction with specific milestone events and/or established control points, it is important that a management system for process safety incorporate requirements for internal monitoring of work performance/accomplishment versus schedule, as well as for interdisciplinary reviews of certain decisions, e.g., major capital investments, design approvals, process and raw material changes, selected variance requests. These latter reviews should be structured so as to allow operating management to draw upon, as needed, the specialized expertise of functional staff in engineering, R&D, medical, legal, and environmental health and safety.

- Variance Procedure. A management system for process safety needs the flexibility to be able to recognize when the existence of special circumstances warrants temporary departures from established operating procedures. It also must have the internal controls to review these departures in advance, for any potentially significant safety risks, and then to limit them in scope and time to ones that can be managed in an acceptable manner.

- Audit Mechanisms. Periodically, chemical process safety programs, including the management system, require a thorough audit of how well they are identifying, assessing, managing, and mitigating significant episodic and chronic process risks. A sound management system will provide for conducting such audits, covering all the technical elements, while focusing primarily on equipment design, operating conditions and procedures, safety systems, and management controls. The system should specify audit frequency as well as how the audits will be performed, e.g., by internal staff, outside consultants, or some combination of the two.

- Corrective Action Mechanisms. When internal reviews or periodic audits identify deficiencies in one or more technical elements of a chemical process safety program, the management system must have the procedures in place to generate, evaluate, select, and implement appropriate, cost-effective technical and/or administrative solutions. These procedures must also provide for subsequent follow-up to determine whether the particular corrective action has successfully removed the deficiency, or if additional measures are required.

- Procedure Renewal and Reauthorization. As processes, technologies and operating environments change over time, there is a need to re-examine and re-evaluate existing operating and control procedures and to modify them as appropriate. A management system for chemical process safety should reflect this need in a formal renewal/reauthorization step in which each major operating and control requirement is periodically subjected to a thorough multidisciplinary review in light of current plant practices and safety performance standards.

APPENDIX B

EXAMPLE SAFETY STANDARD

Subject Operational Readiness Review*	Date: Supersedes Sheet 1 of 3

1.0 SCOPE

This Guideline describes the minimum operational readiness review requirements for all locations.

2.0 PURPOSE

The purpose of this Guideline is to help location management assure safe and economical start-ups and commissionings of new or modified facilities.

3.0 DEFINITIONS

3.1.0 An Operational Readiness Review (ORR) is an onsite pre-startup review, conducted by an ORR team when construction is nearing completion, to help location management assure that sound safety, industrial hygiene, loss prevention and engineering principles have been followed in the facility's design and construction and in its proposed start-up and regular operation.

The ORR helps to assure that safety, industrial hygiene and loss prevention related details agreed upon have been incorporated in the actual construction of the facility and in the proposed start-up, regular and emergency operating procedures and plans.

3.2.0 An ORR Team shall be established for each facility review. The ORR team, guided by location supervisors or engineers, will carry out and report the actual ORR.

4.0 TYPES OF OPERATIONAL READINESS REVIEWS

4.1.0 CORPORATE ORR

A Corporate ORR will be performed on all manufacturing or manufacturing related projects:

a. Of $10,000,000 or more of investment or,

b. Of high levels of risk.

4.1.1 The Corporate ORR Team will be established by the Divisional Line Manufacturing Management and should consist of representatives from the following groups:

- Corporate Safety and Loss Prevention Department
- Corporate Industrial Hygiene Department
- ECD - start-up department
- Research division
- Manufacturing Managers (or nearest equivalent) from other divisions.

Specialists as required e.g., fire protection engineer, security, insurance, and consultants.

4.1.2 The Director of the Safety and Loss Prevention Department, or his designate, will serve as chairman of each corporate ORR Team.

4.1.3 REPORTING

A brief written report will be made within one week of completion of the review. This report will be in addition to a verbal report given to the location manager before the ORR team leaves the plant. The report will be addressed to appropriate senior operating manager or director with copies to the location manager, the Director of the Industrial Hygiene Department; the Director of the Safety and Loss Prevention Department, and others as appropriate.

4.2.0 DIVISION ORR

A Division ORR will be performed on most new or modified facilities, expansions, or process modifications involving up to $10,000,000 of investment.

The necessity of an ORR will be decided by the Divisional Line Manufacturing manager with the concurrence of the Division Loss Prevention manager (or nearest equivalent).

4.2.1 The Division ORR Team will be established by the line manufacturing manager and should consist of representative from the following groups:

Location Engineering

Location Production Management (from another production area or plant).

Specialists as required.

4.2.2 A brief written report will be made within one week of completion of the ORR. The written report will be in addition to a verbal report to the location manage and the project manager before the ORR team leaves the area. The written report will be addressed to the location manager with copies to others as appropriate.

5.0 THE OPERATIONAL READINESS REVIEW (ORR):

5.1.0 A final agenda will be distributed at the location of the new or modified facility. The Location Manager and the Project Manager should be given as much notice as possible so that they may prepare for the review.

5.2.0 Each Committee will conduct Operational Readiness Reviews to determine that sound safety, industrial hygiene, loss prevention, engineering and operating procedures have been followed.

5.3.0 The Reviews will encompass among others:

a. process flow sheets,
b. on-site inspection of equipment and facilities,
c. foreman and operator log books,
d. maintenance procedures,
e. operating instructions and procedures for authorizing revisions,
f. start-up schedule,
g. availability of manpower and level of training,
h. warnings and instructions for response to contingency and emergency conditions.

APPENDIX C

Example of Incident Investigation Guidelines

Outlined below are guidelines for conducting incident investigations. Because of the variety of incidents investigated and the diversity of chemical operations, no attempt is made to provide a mandatory format for use in all situations. Rather, these guidelines represent an example of an effective investigation procedure. The guidelines address the following areas:

1. Incident Reporting
2. Preplanning -- Steps to Take Before an Incident Occurs
3. Management Responsibilities
4. Initial Response
5. Incident Investigation Team
6. Determining the Facts
7. Determining the Cause
8. Recommending Corrective and Preventive Actions
9. Follow-up Systems
10. Communicating Results

1. INCIDENT REPORTING

One cannot investigate incidents if they are not reported. A common reason that incidents go unreported is that, in some organizations, the incident investigation tends to be a search for the "guilty" rather than a search for the facts. When incident investigations are handled as a search for facts, the entire organization is more likely to work together to report incidents and to correct deficiencies, be they procedural, training, human error, managerial, or other.

One must realize that when this approach is adopted, there will likely be an increase in the number of incidents reported. This is good! The objective is to get the situation into the open so the entire organization can work to correct deficiencies and prevent recurrence. With time, one would not necessarily expect a reduction in the frequency of incidents, but certainly a reduction in the frequency of serious incidents.

For reporting purposes, an incident should be viewed as <u>anything that occurs that is unusual or out of the ordinary</u>. Initially, the information to be reported should be limited to what happened (date, time, description, size, impact, etc.) and the action(s) taken. Initial reporting should not be limited to apparently serious or potentially serious incidents because the seriousness cannot always be assessed at the time of occurrence. When all incidents are reported, those that are indeed serious or potentially serious can then be selected for further investigation.

2. PREPLANNING -- STEPS TO TAKE BEFORE AN INCIDENT OCCURS

Effective incident investigation starts before an incident occurs with the establishment of a well-thought-out incident investigation procedure. The importance of preplanning is clearly evident when one understands that the quantity and quality of relevant information begins to diminish immediately following the incident. By establishing the essential stages and steps of an incident investigation ahead of time, the loss of relevant information, through cleanup efforts or possible blurring of people's recollections, can be minimized and/or eliminated.

3. MANAGEMENT RESPONSIBILITIES

Management has a number of important responsibilities that lay the foundation for effective incident investigation. These responsibilities are:

a. To communicate the importance and usefulness of incident investigation as one tool in the control of potential hazards;
b. To create an atmosphere of trust and respect, which in turn leads to openness in reporting of incidents;
c. To provide the resources and priority attention necessary to perform a thorough and comprehensive investigation;
d. To communicate the results to all who may benefit; and
e. To implement systems to ensure that actions are taken on the findings of the incident investigation to prevent recurrence.

4. INITIAL RESPONSE

The initial response to incidents such as fires, releases, explosions, and transportation emergencies should include: (1) providing medical and other safety and health help to personnel, (2) bringing the incident under control, and (3) directing activities related to the investigation in a way that preserves relevant information and evidence.

Activities to preserve information should include: securing and barricading the scene, initiating the collection of transient information, interviewing personnel, etc. Remember that information will begin to disappear or diminish immediately following the incident and the initial response should acknowledge and address this problem. Prompt establishment of incident investigation leadership with priority over operation, maintenance, and construction is vital at this stage.

5. INCIDENT INVESTIGATION TEAM

Prompt establishment of the incident investigation organization is of major importance to the incident investigation. The make-up of the investigation team is another important factor affecting the quality of the investigation. The appointment of competent people reflects management's commitment and helps ensure prompt and effective action during the investigation. The team chairperson should be someone who can effectively:

a. Control the scope of team activities by identifying which lines of investigation should be pursued, referred to another group for study, or deferred;
b. Call and preside over meetings;
c. Assign tasks and establish timetables;
d. Ensure that no potentially useful data source is overlooked; and
e. Keep site management advised of the progress of the investigation.

Although team membership will vary according to the type of incident, a typical team investigating an operating area incident might include:

a. A third-line or higher supervisor from the section where the incident occurred;
b. Personnel from an area not involved in the incident;
c. Engineering and/or maintenance personnel;
d. The safety supervisor;
e. A first-line supervisor from the affected area;
f. Occupational health/environmental personnel;
g. Appropriate wage personnel (i.e., operators, mechanics, technicians); and
h. Research and/or technical personnel.

It is also appropriate to consider and include other specialists and/or consultants either on a part-time or full-time basis.

6. DETERMINING THE FACTS

A thorough and comprehensive search for the facts is a necessary step in the incident investigation. During the fact-finding phase of the investigation, team members should:

a. Visit the incident scene before the physical evidence is disturbed.
b. Sample unknown spills, vapors, residues, etc., noting conditions which may have affected the sample.
c. Prepare visual aids, such as photographs, field sketches, missile maps and other graphical representations with the objective of providing data for the investigation.
d. Obtain on-the-spot information from eyewitnesses, if possible. Interviews with those directly involved and others whose input might be useful should be scheduled soon thereafter. The interviews should be conducted privately and individually, so that the comments of one witness will not influence the response of others.
e. Observe "key" mechanical equipment as it is disassembled.
f. Review all sources of potentially useful information. These may include as-built drawings, operating logs, recorder charts, previous reports, procedures, equipment manuals, oral instructions, change of design records indicating the

previous training and performance of the employees involved, computer simulations, laboratory tests, etc.

g. Determine which incident-related items should be preserved. When a preliminary analysis reveals that an item may have failed to operate correctly, was damaged, etc., arrangements should be made to either preserve the item or carefully document any subsequent repairs or modifications.
h. Carefully document the sources of information contained in the incident report. This will be valuable should it subsequently be determined that further study of the incident or potential incident is necessary.

7. DETERMINING THE CAUSE

Establishing the basic cause(s) of an incident is crucial to development of effective recommendations to correct and prevent a recurrence. Many methods can be used to sort out the facts, inferences, and judgements assembled by the investigation team. Even for incidents for which the cause appears obvious, formal analysis is recommended as protection against oversight or making premature and erroneous judgements. Outlined below is one approach that can be used to develop the cause and effect relationships.

a. Develop the "chronology of events" which occurred before, during, and after the incident. The focus of the chronology should be solely on what happened and what actions were taken. List alternatives when the status cannot be definitely established because of missing or contradictory information.
b. Identify conditions or circumstances which deviated from normal, no matter how insignificant they may seem.
c. Identify all hypotheses of the causes of the incident based on these deviations.
d. Test the hypotheses against all available evidence and information, and list in order of likelihood.
e. A "cause tree" approach similar to a "fault tree" can be somewhat helpful in depicting the many different failures that led to the incident under investigation. The "cause tree" helps ensure that failures are reduced to more basic or fundamental initiating events.

Another source to consult for help in focusing on the cause(s) of an incident in the National Safety Council's Corrective Action Identification Procedure.

8. RECOMMENDING CORRECTIVE AND PREVENTIVE ACTIONS

Usually, recommendations for corrective and preventive actions follow in a rather straightforward manner from the cause(s) after they have been determined. A recommendation for corrective action has three important parts. The first is the recommendation itself, which describes the actions to be taken to prevent a recurrence of the incident. The second is the name of the person or position responsible for completing the recommendation. The third is the timing for completion of the recommendation.

A number of recommendations may be prerequisites for safe operation, and thus will require completion prior to resuming operations. Others will involve areas needing additional work or study or may involve problems not directly related to the incident. For these timing would extend beyond resumption of operations.

9. FOLLOW-UP SYSTEM

To ensure follow-up and closure of recommendations from an incident investigation, it is important to develop and implement a system to address open recommendations and to document actions taken to close out recommendations. Such a system should include periodic status reports to site management.

10 COMMUNICATING RESULTS

Two additional essential steps in the effort to prevent recurrence of an incident are (1) documentation of the incident investigation findings and (2) review of the results of the investigation with appropriate personnel.

The incident documentation should address the following topics:

a. Description of the incident (including date, time and location);
b. Facts determined during investigation (including chronology as appropriate);
c. Statement of cause(s); and
d. Recommendations for corrective and preventive action (including timing and responsibility for completion).

Results of the incident investigation should be reviewed with appropriate operating, maintenance, and other personnel whose work assignments are within the facility where the incident occurred. Also, depending on the seriousness of the incident, consideration should be given to reviewing results with other similar facilities to prevent occurrence there.

Source: Reference 65

BIBLIOGRAPHY

1. A Guide to Hazard and Operability Studies, Chemical Industries Association, 1977.
2. Advisory Committee on Major Hazards, First Report, London: HMSO, 1976.
3. Ale, B., Risk Assessment and the Safety of the Public," Ministry of Housing, Physical Planning and Environment, Leidschendam, The Netherlands, 1984.
4. Ansoff, H. Igor, Implementing Strategic Management, Englewood Cliffs, NJ, Prentice- Hall International, 1984.
5. Anthony, Robert N., Management Control Systems, Homewood, IL, Richard D. Irwin, Inc., 1984.
6. Anthony, Robert N., The Management Control Function, Boston, MA, The Harvard Business School Press, 1988.
7. Asbjornsen, O.A., Technical Management: A Major Challenge in Industrial Competition, Chem. Eng. Prog., Nov. 1988, pp. 27-32.
8. API 510 Pressure Vessel Inspection Code: Maintenance Inspection, Rating, Repair, and
   Alteration, Fourth Edition, American Petroleum Institute, Washington, DC, 1985.
9. API-620 Recommended Rules for Design and Construction of Large, Welded, Low Pressure Storage Tanks, Seventh Edition, American Petroleum Institute, Washington, DC, 1985.
10. ASME Boiler and Pressure Vessel Code, Section VIII, Rules for Construction of Pressure Vessels, Division I, American Society of Mechanical Engineers, New York, 1983 Edition.
11. Baybutt, P., Communicating Risk Step by Step, Hydrocarbon Processing, Vol. 68, No. 6, 1989, p. 85
12. Burk, A.F., Managing Process Safety to Prevent Catastrophes, Industrial Hygiene Management, Ch. 9, Wiley, 1988.
13. Camillus, John C., Strategic Planning and Management Control, Lexington, MA, Lexington Books, 1986.
14. CCPS Guidelines for Process Equipment Reliability Data with Data Tables, AIChE/CCPS, 1989
15. Chemical Plant and Petroleum Refinery Piping - ANSI/ASME B31.3, American Society of Mechanical Engineers, New York, 1984.
16. Control of Chemicals in IBM Facilities, IBM Corporate Standard C-S 3-0527-002, 1987.

17. Crosby, Philip B., Quality without Tears, New York, McGraw-Hill, 1984.
18. Deming, W. Edwards, Out of the Crisis, M.I.T. Center for Advanced Engineering Studies, Cambridge, MA, 1986.
19. Dermer, Jerry, Management Planning and Control Systems, Homewood, IL, Richard D. Irwin, Inc., 1977.
20. DeSteese, J.G., Human Factors Affecting the Reliability and Safety of LNG (Liquefied Natural Gas) Facilities: Vol. 1 - Control Panel Design Enhancement and Vol. 2 - Control Panel Design Guidelines and Checklist, Battelle Pacific Northwest Labs, prepared for Gas Research Institute, PB83-188599 and 188607, January 1983.
21. DIERS, DIERS Project Manual, AIChE, 1988.
22. Eilon, Samuel, Management Control, London, MacMillan and Company, Ltd., 1971.
23. Feigenbaum, Armand V., Total Quality Control, Third Edition, New York, McGraw- Hill, 1983.
24. Fire & Explosion Index: Hazard Classification Guide, Chem. Eng. Prog., Technical Manual, Sixth Edition, AIChE, 1987.
25. Frontiers in Chemical Engineering: Research Needs and Opportunities, Chem. Eng. Prog., Dec. 1988.
26. Garrett, J.T., et al. (eds.), New Perspectives in Management Control, New York, St. Martin's Press, 1983
27. Garvan, David A., Managing Quality, Novato, CA, Freeperson Press, 1987.
28. Greeno, J.L., Hedstrom, G.S., DiBerto, M.A., Environmental Auditing: Fundamentals and Techniques (Second Edition), Arthur D. Little, Inc., Wiley & Sons, New York, 1987, pp. 1-368.
29. Greeno, J.L., Hedstrom, G.S., DiBerto, M.A., The Environmental, Health, and Safety Auditor's Handbook, Arthur D. Little, Inc., 1988, pp. 1-220.
30. Guide for Inspection of Refinery Equipment, American Petroleum Institute, Washington, DC, 1957.
31. Guide to Reducing Human Error in Process Operation (short version), Safety and Reliability Directorate, SRD R 347, February 1985.
32. Guidelines for Chemical Process Quantitative Risk Analysis, AIChE/CCPS, 1989.
33. Guidelines for Hazard Evaluation Procedures, AIChE/CCPS, 1985.
34. Guidelines for Human Reliability in Process Safety, AIChE/CCPS, Oct. 1989.
35. Guidelines for Management of Process Hazards, Recommended Practice (currently not specified), American Petroleum Institute, Washington, D.C., 1988.
36. Hanna, S.R., Guidelines for Use of Vapor Cloud Dispersion Models, AIChE/CCPS, 1987.
37. Harrington, H. James, The Improvement Process: How America's Leading Companies Improve Quality, New York, McGraw-Hill, 1986.
38. Hayes, Glenn E., and Romig, Harry G., Modern Quality Control, Revised Edition, Mission Hills, CA, Glencoe Publication Co., 1982.
39. Hayes, Glenn E., Quality and Productivity: The New Challenge, Quality and Productivity Conference Proceedings, Society of Automotive Engineers, 1985.
40. Hope, S., et al., Methodologies for Hazard Analysis and Risk Assessment in the Petroleum Refining and Storage Industry, Concawe, Risk Assessment Group, the Hague, Report No. 10/82, 1982.
41. Human Detection and Diagnosis of System Failures, Rasmussen, J., and Rouse, W., eds. Plenum Press, 1981.

42. Ishikawa, Kaoru, What is Total Quality Control? The Japanese Way, Englewood Cliffs, NJ, ASQC Quality Press, Prentice Hall, 1985.
43. Ishikawa, Kaoru, Guide to Quality Control, Asian Productivity Organization, Tokyo, Unipub, 1982.
44. Kletz, Trevor A., Cheaper, Safer Plants or Wealth and Safety at Work, The Institute of Chemical Engineers, Rugby, Warks, England, 1984, p. 97.
45. Kletz, Trevor A., HAZOP & HAZAN, Notes on the Identification and Assessment of Hazards, The Institution of Chemical Engineers, Rugby, Warks, England.
46. Kletz, Trevor, A., The Prevention of Major Leaks - Better Inspection after Construction, presented at the 17th AIChE Loss Prevention Symposium, Denver, CO, August 1983.
47. Kletz, Trevor A., What Went Wrong? Case Histories of Process Plant Disasters, Gulf Publishing, Houston, TX, 1985, pp. 30-45.
48. LeVine, R., Guidelines for Safe Storage and Handling of High Toxic Hazard Materials, AIChE/CCPS, New York, 1988.
49. Lees, Frank P., Loss Prevention in the Process Industries: Hazard Identification, Assessment and Control, Vol. 2, London and Boston, Butterworths, 1980, pp. 738-745.
50. Lihach, N., Designing for Man-Advances in Control Room Operations, EPRI Journal, July/August 1982, pp. 6-13.
51. Lowe, T., and Maehin, J. (eds.), New Perspectives in Management Control, New York, St. Martin's Press, 1983.
52. Marciariello, Joseph A., Management Control Systems, Englewood Cliffs, NJ, Prentice-Hall, Inc., 1984.
53. Martinott, R.T., Maintenance Management Systems, Chemical Week, March 9, 1988, pp. 20-24.
54. Mautz, R.K., and Winjum, J., Criteria for Management Control Systems, New York, Financial Executives Research Foundation, 1981.
55. Merchant, Kenneth A., Control in Business Organization, Plano, TX, Business Publications, Inc., 1985.
56. Merrick, Robert D., Materials Consideration in Loss Prevention, presented at the API Conference, Fundamental Applications of Loss Prevention, Houston, TX, October 1985.
57. Munson, R.E., Process Hazards Management in DuPont, Plant/Operations Progress, Vol. 4, No. 1, January 1985, pp. 13-16.
58. Overview - A Total Management Program for Loss Prevention and Control, Industrial Risk Insurers, Hartford, Conn., 1986, pp. 1-91.
59. Ozog, H., and Bendixen, L.M., Hazard Identification and Quantification, Chem. Eng. Prog., Vol. 83, No. 4, April 1987, pp. 55-64.
60. Parry, S.T., A Review of Hazard Identification Techniques and Their Application to Major Accident Hazards, U.K. Atomic Emergency Authority, Safety and Reliability Directorate, SRD R 379, March 1986.
61. Perry's, Chemical Engineers' Handbook, Sixth Edition, London, McGraw-Hill, 1984.
62. Process Safety Management (Control of Acute Hazards), Chemical Manufacturers Association, May 1985.
63. Prugh, Richard W., and Johnson, R.W., Guidelines for Vapor Release Mitigation, AIChE/CCPS, New York, NY, 1988.

64. Rausch, Douglas A., Operating Discipline: A Key to Safety, Chem. Eng. Prog., June 1986, pp. 13-15.
65. Recommendations for Process Hazards Management of Substances with Catastrophic Potential Organization Resources Counselors, Inc., 1988.
66. Ross, Philip F., Taguchi Techniques for Quality Engineering, New York, McGraw-Hill, 1988.
67. Sanders, Roy E., Plant Modifications: Troubles and Treatment, Chem. Eng. Prog., February 1983, pp. 73-77.
68. Schoderbek, P., et al., Management Systems: Conceptual Considerations, Plano, TX, Business Publications, Inc., 1985.
69. Smith, R.A., Process Safety, Summer National Meeting, AIChE, 1988.
70. Stoner, James A.F., and Wankel, Charles, Management, Englewood Cliffs, NJ, Prentice- Hall, Inc., 1986.
71. Whiston, J., and Eddershaw, B., Quality and Safety - Distant Cousins or Close Relatives, The Chemical Engineer, June 1989, pp. 97-102.
72. Woolfulk, W.H., and Sanders, R.E., Dynamic Testing and Maintenance of Safety Relief Valves, Chemical Engineering, October 26, 1987, pp. 119-124.
73. Workbook of Test Cases for Vapor Cloud Source Dispersion Models, AIChE/CCPS, 1989.

INDEX